The WORLD at CHRISTMAS

The WORLD at Christmas

Charles house

THE BRUCE PUBLISHING CO • NEW YORK

Library of Congress Catalog Card Number: 68-56623

The Bruce Publishing Company, New York
Collier-Macmillan Canada, Ltd., Toronto, Ontario
Made in the United States of America

CONTENTS

PREFACE

This is a story of historical fact and fanciful fiction, all tumbled together. The meticulous care of the historian has been coupled with the fantasies and the fibs of the story teller, and all to a purpose.

The purpose? It is to help the reader see into the Christmas customs of many places in the world, and to introduce him briefly to some of the people and creatures which have been part of the story of the festival. Christmas has traveled some strange paths in its development from the birth of Christ to the mailing of Christmas cards. Sometimes, too, it has sailed back in time, all of its own, to pick up and bring along some weird and awful creatures from the days when people were frightened and wanted to be frightened because they knew no better.

That Christmas should have gathered unto itself some baleful and eerie creatures from the days of the pagans is curious. Christmas is such a sweet and joyous time that monsters and demons really ought not to belong. But they have belonged to it, dragged into it by the heels for the sole purpose of frightening children into obedience.

These characters are at least as real as the fairies and the elves and the trolls and the little goblins, and as real as Santa Claus. Legend contrives to embellish them with reality, but it should not be permitted. Legend must be legend; fact must be fact.

I trust that the fact and fiction as presented here may be easily separated, even by the most gullible. If there are some portions of the book which do not adequately present fact as fact and fiction as fiction in such a manner then it must be laid to the author's carelessness or ignorance. But in his pursuit of knowledge, he learned something about the people of 35 different countries, all shared here.

But if the story leads the reader into a better understanding of the things which the wide world has done to Christmas — the good and the bad things — then my purpose has been accomplished.

Let it also be said that there is no such thing as the magical Transvolo Stone which I have employed as a device to get me from country to country all within a single Christmas period. There is no Transvolo Stone; I wish to make that clear. At least, there isn't one now.

1

AN ESCORT FROM GREECE

I DID not think my first attempt to use the un-
natural powers of the Transvolo Stone would
be such a dreadful success, but it was. When I
awakened on that frosty, clear December morning, I glanced quite naturally at the old stone
in my back yard. The Kallikantzeros was there. Ugly, beast-
like and horrifying, he lolled on the old rock and made what
he may have thought were funny faces, but they were not.

His blood-red tongue hung loosely from his mouth like a
gaudy banner. His eyes were yellow-amber in color, and they
glowed like hot coals. His elongated body, wolf-like in general configuration, was covered with coarse, black hair.

I did not go immediately to speak with him for fear of
what the neighbors might think if they could see us in conversation. Perhaps, though, they could not see him. I wished
that I could not.

"Some Christmas!" I thought ruefully.

I also thought belatedly that perhaps I should not have
tried to evoke the powers of the Transvolo Stone by learning
and reciting the ancient incantations which activated its powers. But now it was too late. The Kallikantzeros awaited me.

I am quite certain that it is best if I do not reveal here the
specific words which I used in the incantation. I am also quite
sure that a detailed discussion about the Transvolo Stone and

its powers will serve no good purpose. After my experimental attempts to visit the world at Christmastime, I will try to forget the Stone. Perhaps in another century, another age, it may be rediscovered and put to use. But I do not think so.

I know very little about the Transvolo Stone. Its Latin name means "to fly over, or across," but of course it had other names in other centuries. I do not know them, though. Nor do I know how it came to be in my backyard. Perhaps it was always there. At any rate, I used it to request a magical passage to Greece in time to observe the Christmas festival. I had no idea, of course, that I would be provided with an escort of the Kallikantzeroi family. But it was my first effort to use the storied powers of the Transvolo Stone. First efforts often are drenched with error.

The Kallikantzeroi are demonic Christmas creatures who are mischievous and sometimes malevolent. Their chief pastime is terrorizing superstitious Greek peasants during the Twelve Days of Christmas. They play pranks in sheer, wanton mischief and, taken altogether, they are a curious manifestation in a Christmas festival. Nevertheless, they have been part of the folklore of Greece for many centuries.

2

And, if I were to get my wish to journey to Greece during the time when the Kallikantzeroi are out, I would apparently have to speak with the outrageous creature who was there even now sitting on the Transvolo Stone in my back yard. If such creatures as these are part of the Grecian Christmas festival, it was clearly my duty to learn what I could learn. I could have wished for a more charming companion. When you have a guest from a foreign country, however, you do your best to be polite.

2

CHRISTMAS IN GREECE

EGARDLESS of the presence of my unattractive companion, the almost instantaneous journey to the place of ancient glory, the once great city of Sparta, was a brisk pleasure. I heard a "whoosh" and we were there. The Kallikantzeros led me down a rubbled street in a back section of Sparta to the home of citizen Spyros Papadiamandis and his small family.

The Kallikantzeros told me, in bad grace, that Spyros was 27 years old, short and plump, and married to a dark-haired, dark-eyed woman who was somewhat shorter and somewhat more plump than her husband. They had two children, the ill-mannered Kallikantzeros told me — Nikos and Demetrios. Good names.

Spyros and his wife, Rhea, lived in a tiny stone house with a tile roof. Two sheep were tethered in the backyard. We walked down the short path to the doorway and stopped. The Kallikantzeros frowned fearfully as I lifted my right hand to knock.

"Wait," he said. "Spyros has taken some measures to keep me out of his house. It's a show of discourtesy that he will regret."

My ugly companion stepped back to the fence which encompassed the Papadiamandis house and yard. Then, unceremoniously, he tore the front gate from its hinges and cast it into the gravel road. He came back to me on the doorstep, pleased with the damage he had done. He smirked.

"I can't enter the house because of this sign," the Kallikantzeros said as he pointed to a symbol on the upper panel of the entrance. It was a cross marked with black fireplace ashes.

"Never mind," he said. "At the time of Christmas — the Twelve Days, you know — the people of Greece are unusually careful about barring me from their homes. Spyros is more careful than most because he is the pottery maker in town. Last year I got into his workshop and broke 43 water pitchers he had just finished. I finished them completely."

It was apparently a pleasant memory for the vandalous fellow. He laughed unpleasantly at the recollection.

"Spyros forgets that I have other means of entry," he said. "Wait one moment before you knock on the door. I'll see you inside."

Without another word he leaped to the eaves of the house, then pulled himself up onto the tile roof. There, almost cat-like, he scurried to the chimney.

I waited no longer. I was not willing to help him do his notorious mischief. I knocked.

Spyros himself answered. He was rather shorter than I thought he might be because I think of Greeks as tall and soldier-lean, but his smile was broad and cheerful. He welcomed me with splendid Grecian hospitality which I expected of such a noble people. He grasped my hand warmly and with such a show of pleasure that I felt comfortable and almost at home.

Spyros then presented me with an olive branch, a symbol I thought, and he spoke to me in the language of the modern Greek. I do not ordinarily understand the Greek language, but something had happened to my perception and somehow I knew what he said. It was easy for me to guess that my understanding was part of my journey. I did not question the new skill which was given to me, I suppose, by the magic of the Transvolo Stone.

Without waiting to be introduced to Rhea and the two dark-eyed sons who stood in the background, I gave Spyros the signal which means "shhh!" in every land in the world. With forefinger touching my lips, I pointed with my other hand toward the upper element of his chimney place and whispered the word, "Kallikantzeros!" I was not certain he would understand my pronunciation.

But he did. He turned pale. Quickly then he smiled, showing even, white teeth and more happiness than I could have mustered under similar conditions.

"It's okay," he said in English. (Okay has become a universal word.) "We are prepared."

Spyros turned expansively and introduced me first to his children and then to his wife, Rhea. Their smiles were genuine, infectious and comforting. The Spartan of the modern day is extremely jolly, talkative, gregarious and hospitable. He is greatly different from the citizen-soldier Spartan of history who was so austere and brave that the word Spartan has come into our language as a description of those qualities.

The home of the Papadiamandis family was humble by some standards, but it was interesting. The fireplace was clearly the most important element of the simple room. Kettles and pots and pans were strewn around the fireplace in some disarray. The air was heavy with the smell of a mixture of meats, including pork.

The kitchen table was large enough for a big family. It had a hand-made appearance as did the chairs which surrounded it. I noted that there were five places set at the table. Apparently the Kallikantzeros was either not invited or unwelcome, but I had been expected.

6

I frowned to my host. Once again I pointed to the chimney top and whispered the name of my sinister escort.

The family laughed together. Spyros took me by the hand and guided me to the fireplace. Then, bending over, he pointed a finger upwards into the fireplace. I leaned over and looked up. I saw three pork bones hanging there, and several long, dark sausages.

"These keep the Kallikantzeroi out," he said. "They serve as guards. Besides, the village priest will walk by in a moment to purify him away from here. The priest will use water from last year's blessing. The good in it has not been used up."

From the roof I heard a mumbling, unpleasant chant which I guessed from its simplicity was hundreds of years old. It was in the voice, now a dolorous one, of the Kallikantzeros.

> "Quick I go, begone! I must be gone!
> Here comes the pot-bellied priest
> With his censer in his hand
> And his sprinkling vessel, too.
> He has purified the streams
> And he has purified me. I go!"

We looked out of the smoky window. The priest was indeed moving up the little street with a censer and sprinkler which was working its charms. The Kallikantzeros was retreating on all fours. Swiftly!

When I urged Spyros and Rhea to tell me why they allowed such a demoniacal being to be part of their Christmas festival, the most beautiful and charming one of the year, they had no good answer. Rhea simply shrugged her shoulders and Spyros answered with a single word: "Nightmares." I thought perhaps the strange fear that modern Greek peasants hold for the imaginary man-beast may have its background in the ancient festi-

7

vals of winter during the days of Dionysus. It was then the custom for people to wear dreadful masks and to parade in the night. But perhaps the real reason for permitting the Kallikantzeroi to spoil a lovely Christmas is lost in antiquity.

"I have come to observe how you spend your Christmas," I told Spyros, "but yet I do not see a Christmas tree. When do you put it up?"

"Christmas tree?" he asked. He turned to look at Rhea but her perplexed look told me that the people of Greece simply do not use the Christmas tree as a symbol of the season. I moved my hand to indicate that he should not bother to answer, but he was a good host. He tried.

"Tree?" he asked softly. "Tree?" Then once again he showed me his warm smile. He hurried to the corner where he pointed to a copper kettle. Grinning, he indicated that I should look inside. There, hanging by a small wire looped over the rim of the kettle, was a sprig of basil wound around a small wooden cross. A few inches of water remained in the kettle.

"I do not understand," I said as courteously as I could. I had no intention of hurting this pleasant man's feelings.

Spyros beckoned Rhea to his side. She took the sprig-and-cross, dipped it into the water and moved about the room sprinkling the special water everywhere.

"This," said Spyros in Greek, "is one of our means of keeping the Kallikantzeroi out of the house, out of the corners." He had apparently thought in botanical terms when I said "Christmas tree." The basil had occured to him. Basil is a sweet herb of the mint family. It is characterized by a pleasant, aromatic smell and taste, but it is not very much like a Christmas tree! Perhaps it was named in honor of St. Basil.

Here we were concerned with the Kallikantzeroi again! Would I not hear the end of this imaginary creature?

"But," I said gently, "I see none of the trappings of Christmas here. Don't you observe the ancient festival?"

"The sun goes down soon," said Spyros, "and you shall see."

Rhea was busy at the fireplace. I glanced at her, then looked hard. She was burning old shoes! The meaty odor which had filled the room when I entered was now masked under the sharp, acrid smell of smoking leather.

I looked at Spyros with a question in my eyes.

"It drives away the Kallikantzeroi," he explained seriously. I gestured as though to dismiss the subject, but Spyros insisted: "He plays evil jokes on us," he said. "He smashes things. He breaks furniture and dishes. He is never happier than when he causes misfortune or unhappiness with his mischief. You shall see. The Kallikantzeros will play a bad trick on you, too. This I can promise."

The two Papadiamandis boys were getting ready to leave the house. Although the weather was reasonably warm — about 50 degrees — they buttoned their jackets and put on their hats.

"You are invited to join Nikos and Demetrios," Spyros told me. I left the house with them. At the broken gateway there was a large, happy group of young boys.

9

I wandered with them, walking a few yards behind and listening to the transcendent beauty of their child voices in songs of reverence. The hours wore on and on, as the children visited every home in Sparta which, these days, is scarcely the size of the Sparta of old. Once a great city, today Sparta is merely a small town, an old one which dates to 1100 B.C.

At each home, the master of the house came out and thanked the children for their songs and handed out little packages of dried figs, almonds, walnuts and sweet cookies. A boy with a drum and another with a small, tinkling triangle which gave forth chime-like sounds were always best rewarded.

I thought how different were the faces of these modern Spartans from the faces I had seen on the statues and the paintings of old! It is true that there is scarcely a drop of old Hellenic blood left in the charming Greeks of today. Old Greece was overrun for some two thousand years, mainly by Slavic people. Old Greece has faded away, and modern Greece and the gay, gregarious, charming but volatile Grecians of today are on the threshold of new adventure.

Suddenly I was out of the procession. From somewhere behind me, a melon was flung at my head — by a good marksman. I went down, stunned. Nikos helped me to my feet.

"The Kallikantzeros!" he said angrily. And, of course, it was. Nikos helped me home.

By four o'clock in the morning the boys returned. They were laden with good things to eat and they were in a jolly, noisy mood and not yet ready for bed.

Bed? Not in Greece on Christmas eve! Now was the time — at this strange hour — to go to Mass. Notwithstanding my melancholy headache, I joined the family as we visited their church, new to me — the Greek Orthodox. The services were beautiful and inspiring.

At last, filled with sweet reverence and great joy, we returned

10

home. And I had become greatly fond of this dear family of modern Greeks. But it was not yet time for bed although the hour was 5:30 a.m. Now was the hour, they said, to eat and to have friends and relatives in for a noisy, gay visit.

Someone once said that Greeks are either "feasting or fasting," and this, as I could see, was clearly a feast. Rhea was preparing Christmas delicacies, including yearling lamb (arni), but it was the custom of her family to prepare it out of doors and on a spit. To accompany the roast lamb was a delicate wine perfectly suited to it (roditys) which is served at least three times a year when the traditional Greeks are festive. The special times are at Christmas, on St. George's Day, April 23, and, always and most important, at Easter.

Rhea also prepared stuffed grape leaves (dolmades) and, of course, the strange, syrupy coffee (kafes) which the Greeks love. I observed her method of making the sweet variety.

She used two cups of water, six lumps of sugar, six heaping teaspoons of finely ground coffee. Deftly into the fireplace she placed the pot containing the water and sugar only. She let it rise to a boil. Now she removed the kettle and stirred the coffee into it. Then it went back into the fireplace and was boiled once more.

Rhea did not speak often to me though she jabbered almost incessantly at her husband and at the boys. She was exhorting them to tell me to observe her techniques at making this very strong coffee. After it had boiled once more, she removed it and skimmed off the foam which had risen to the top. Carefully, she placed the foam in a smaller pot. Again the coffee went back into the fireplace and was brought once more to a boil. And once more she skimmed off the foam and placed it in the smaller pot. Rhea now added one teaspoon of cold water and, lo! the kafe was ready to serve.

Rhea raised her dark eyebrows and looked to me as though

11

asking if I would try some of the coffee of which she was so proud. I smiled and nodded. It was thick and strong, almost of the consistency of syrup.

Rhea dipped a little of the foam out of the small pot and placed a teaspoon of it into each demitasse. "The foam is very important," she said, "because it contains the luck of the coffee." Then she poured each small cup full of the heavy black brew.

The coffee, even so little of it, made me dizzy with its potency, but I smiled as best I could and nodded, appreciatively I hoped. Rhea beamed.

I was to learn later that Greek families, when they have guests, and Greek restaurants, make coffee in three different ways. One must know how to ask for the kind one wishes.

Metroi vastro is medium boiled and medium sweetened. Vary glyko means strong and sweet — like Rhea's. Sketto vastro is coffee without sugar.

Each kind must be served, Rhea said, in a long handled, lipped Turkish coffee pot which is called a briki.

I am sure that I will never become addicted to Greek coffee. My head swam from the potency of it.

The sturdy table was precious with pomegranates, tangerines, nuts, and cakes called kourabiedes and Christpsomo (bread of Christ). Christpsomo is a plain but delicious cake decorated with nuts. The kourabiedes are small cakes covered with powdered sugar. When they are soaked in diluted honey, Spyros said, they are called melomacaroma.

"When does the Greek family give the presents?" I asked, and immediately I felt that I might have been clumsy with my question and may have seemed greedy.

"What presents?" Spyros asked, curious.

"Well, you know, *Christmas presents.*"

"Where did you hear that this is the day to receive presents?" Rhea asked.

"The Kallikantzeros told me."

"Ha!" said Spyros. "We give presents not on Christmas but on St. Basil's Day in June! You must come then."

I smiled wearily to myself, picked up the modest but splendid present Spyros had given me when I first came to his house, and I felt happy enough. It was an olive branch, eternal, universal symbol of friendship and peace.

I do not know how I returned home. Suddenly I was there and soon in bed, but unable to sleep. Too much coffee. I arose, went to the Transvolo Stone and muttered the formula which I had accidentally discovered. I made a wish to go to Scandinavia. Then I went back to bed.

3

STRAINED FOREIGN
RELATIONS

HEN I glanced out of the window the next day I was astounded at what I saw. I realized in quick, dull horror that I had made a foolish mistake. Outside on the Transvolo Stone there were four Christmas people. They were sitting in stiff-necked, smoldering rage. Four people! I wondered about the possibility of sending three of them away. I did not know how this could be done tactfully.

I donned my warm topcoat and a furry hat and walked out to the Stone in what I hoped appeared to be a cordial manner. I introduced myself courteously and waited.

"Glaedelig Yul!" said a tiny gnome-like man with button bright eyes. "I am the Jultomten of Sweden."

"Happy Yuletide, Jultomten!" I said politely.

"And I," said another small person who was very like a pocket-size Santa Claus, "am the Julenisse."

"Of?"

"Of Norway," he said.

"I am Nisse, of Denmark," said another gnome-like man who resembled the Jultomten. His clothing was very like the clothing worn by the American Santa Claus. Much smaller, of course, because the Nisse was scarcely two feet tall.

I turned to the fourth Christmas personality, a strange, small

14

man dressed in the costume of a goat. A set of handsome horns was mounted on his head. I waited for him to speak but he sulked. At last when he did speak, his voice came muffled from beneath the goat's head he wore. His manner made it clear that his feelings were wounded.

"I am the Joulupukki," he said almost disdainfully. And he quickly added, "I came from Finland but I am the real, the true, the only Father Christmas." He raised his left hand which was covered with the skin and cloven hoof of a goat. He was about to speak again, but, to my surprise, the Norwegian Julenisse broke into a Christmas song. It was, I thought, somewhat rude of him, but then he is a mischievous man. I could only wait until he had finished.

The Joutomten stared. He said, "Tull øg Toys!" ("Stuff and nonsense!").

I told him that it was not very polite for the Julenisse to

interrupt while the Joulupukki was speaking.

"But he is forevermore complaining," said the Julenisse of Norway. "And furthermore, he certainly is not the real and the only Father Christmas. I am."

"Negative!" said the Jultomten. "I am."

"I think not," said the Nisse of Denmark. "I am."

"Ba-a-a-a-a!" said the Finnish goatman derisively.

"Listen to me, good people," I told them. "This is all my fault and I am sorry for it. But I do not think it is going to help any of us if you just sit there and quibble."

"We will not quibble," said the Joulupukki. "Nevertheless, I am the Father Christmas. You should not have invited the others."

"No," said the Julenisse. "But I am Father Christmas!"

"Hold it!" I said more sharply than is polite. "We will stop here and now. I wanted to go to the Scandinavian countries but I will not go if it causes you to sit here and quarrel. I am going into the house and I will not come back until you stop quarreling and treating each other unkindly. When I come out, I hope you will have the matter settled. Only then shall I agree to travel to Scandinavia."

I walked into the house. There I sat and reflected on the cause of the mixup.

When I made my magic incantations at the Transvolo Stone I had asked only that I be permitted to go "to Scandinavia." I simply and erroneouly thought of Scandinavia as being a single place. It is not. My four guests and their attitudes were evidence that it is not.

Fundamentally, the word "Scandinavia" refers to the Scandinavian peninsula which is a wide territory bordered on the east by the Baltic Sea and on the north and west by the Arctic, the North Atlantic and the North Sea. If we think strictly in

16

terms of geography, "Scandinavia" includes Norway and Sweden only. But the world does not think geographically when using the generic term "Scandinavia."

Thinking the matter over in my living room, I reflected that although Denmark is not situated on the Scandinavian peninsula, most people like to place it within the loose definition of Scandinavia. Neither is Finland on the peninsula, but almost everybody naturally places it within the special embrace of Scandinavia.

The Finns have such a close relationship in language, history and racial background to the Swedes, Norwegians and Danes that it simply belongs to the group. Finland was, in fact, part of the Swedish Empire from about 1157, when King Eric IX of Sweden led a crusade to Finland and conquered the Finnish tribes, until 1808.

Hence I was sorry that I had been so general in my request at the Transvolo Stone. I was now embarrassed at having called four representatives of Scandinavian Christmas to my backyard. I now knew that I should have chosen each of those splendid countries individually and in turn. But what could I do now that I had made my foolish error of grouping them all as one?

I glanced out of the window to see how my guests were faring. I was greatly dismayed to discover that they were gone. I walked outside to the Stone. I stood there momentarily and complained to myself.

"Some Christmas!" I said.

I was startled by a voice coming from the Stone.

"Some Christmas indeed!" The phrase seemed pleasant, friendly.

It was the voice of the Julenisse of Norway.

"Where are you, Julenisse?" I asked the atmosphere.

"I am here," said the voice near the Transvolo Stone, "but I am now as all men know me. I am not to be seen by mankind."

"Can nobody see you . . . not ever?"

"Yes," he replied. "Do you have a cat?"

"I have given it to friends temporarily. Why a cat?"

"Cats are the only creatures in the world who have the gift of seeing me. But on this occasion and for this purpose only, I will become visible to you as I was earlier. Nobody else. Do you understand?"

I thanked him and he became visible.

"But the other Scandinavians. Where are they?"

"I have arranged that you will go first to Norway. After that, we shall see. The others are not pleased about it."

"Will you wait for me a few moments?" I asked. "I will wear my warmest clothing because of the northern latitude of your country."

"Dress comfortably," said the Julenisse, "but remember that Norway has different climates, not all of them sub-arctic. We have a marine climate on the west seacoast, a continental climate in the southeastern parts, and sub-arctic climate in the north and in the mountains.

"The coastal parts of Norway are free of ice due to the warming influence of the Gulf Stream," he said indulgently.

"How cold is it where we are going?"

"We are going to Bekkestua, a suburb of the great city of Oslo. At this moment on this December day, the temperature is exactly . . ."

Then I heard the sound of a great wind and I felt a sense of movement. I knew I was going to witness a Norwegian Christmas. That beautifully mountainous country has been celebrating Christmas since King Haakon the Good established it there about the middle of the 10th century.

18

4

CHRISTMAS IN NORWAY

S THE Julenisse and I arrived at Egne Hjem (My Own Home) Station on the little railway called Trikk, the temperature was 32 degrees F. Of course Norway uses the centigrade system and, said my guide, the temperature was exactly 0 degrees centigrade. He explained a simple formula.

"If you take the actual Fahrenheit temperature and subtract 32 (degrees), then multiply the difference by five-ninths, you have the same temperature in centigrade." He pointed out that if the Fahrenheit temperature is 68, one finds the centigrade temperature like this:

$$68 \text{ degrees Fahrenheit}$$
$$-32$$
$$\overline{}$$
$$36 \times 5/9 = 20 \text{ degrees centigrade}$$

I was pleased to know this formula. But I was curious about the centigrade system.

"The people of the United States and England use the Fahrenheit system which was invented by Gabriel Daniel Fahrenheit, a German physicist," I said. "But who invented the centigrade system?"

Julenisse mumbled something into his wispy beard.

"Pardon me?" I said.

Mumble mumble.

"Was he Norwegian?" I asked.

19

"No."
"Danish?"
"No."
"Finnish?"
"No."
"Then he was Swedish." (He was! Anders Celsius, 1701–1744, was a professor of astronomy at Uppsala University.)

20

The Julenisse seemed to wish to avoid the subject. I was discovering that, although the Scandinavian countries have much in common, each one is proud of its own accomplishments. But I suppose this is one of the most amusing similarities in people all over the world. So I asked no more.

We strolled up a pretty road in Bekkestua, one which bore the long street name, Store Ringeriks-veien. In the near distance, snowcapped mountains loomed and dominated the exciting landscape.

Julenisse poked a thumb at one mountain, now lit by the golden light of a setting sun, and said, "That's Oskartoppen. It means Oscar's Top."

He pointed to another nearby range. "That's Kolsaas, or Kol's Mountain."

As we strolled along Store Ringeriks-veien, the Julenisse sang the Norwegian version of the beautiful "Silent Night." He was, as you know, a tiny gnome-like man, and his voice, therefore, was reedlike, thin and sweet.

> Glade jul, hellige jul,
> Engler daler ned i skjul,
> Englene synger om barnet sa smukt;
> Han har himmeriks dører opplukt,
> Hellig er englenes sang,
> Hellig er englenes sang.

We came to a halt in the front of the home of Mrs. Hjordis Eriksen and her three children, Magne, Ødd and Berit. The Julenisse helped me to try to pronounce the names.

"Pronounce the j in Hjordis as y, Magne as Mogna, Ødd as Awdd and Berit with a rolling r," he said. "It is always polite to speak a person's name properly."

The home was a communally owned apartment house, one of many such kinds in metropolitan areas of Norway.

High on a pole in front of the house was fastened a sheaf

21

of wheat. Similar bunches of grain sheaves decorated the eaves, the roof, and corners of the house. A small garage facing Oygardveien Street was similarly decorated with wheat sheaves.

At my questioning glance, the Julenisse explained. "Today is Julaften or, as you say, Christmas Eve. The good people of my country believe that this is a season for peace and goodwill, not only to all men, but to all of God's creatures. The wheat is always put out as food for the wild birds.

"Just down the street there is the small farm of Gunnar Lunde. Gunnar, like all Norse farmers, will be certain that his horses, his cattle, his goats and his chickens, too, are fed extra portions of the best oats or wheat or barley, because it is Julaften. To forget this extra Christmas season kindness is to bring bad luck to the family for the coming year."

I glanced to the top of the tall pole in the front yard. It was a freshly felled young spruce tree. Branches and twigs had not been cut from its top. This was, the Julenisse told me, to give the birds a place to perch while eating the wheat, their Christmas dinner, and also to give them a measure of protection from the cold winds.

We rang the doorbell at No. 81 on the street named Oygardveien. It was answered by the entire family, with Fru (Mrs.) Hjordis Eriksen in the forefront. Next in order came Berit, Magne and Ødd. They greeted me with great cordiality. I was disturbed that they seemed to have no greeting for my associate, the Julenisse, but then I remembered that he is not usually seen by human beings.

I spoke of this and the Eriksens smiled.

"No, the Julenisse stays in the attic here where he lives and makes mischief throughout the year," said Hjordis. "See, we have already prepared his Christmas dinner." Hjordis pointed to a steaming bowl of food near the stairway to the attic. It had the appearance of a pudding.

22

"It is risengrynsgrøt, a rice porridge with cinammon and butter and sugar," Berit said. "And the Julenisse will eat it. At any rate," she said, "it will be gone by Juledag which is Christmas day."

I had wondered about the Julenisse and his appearance which is not very like the American Santa Claus, but I thought it impolite to ask the Julenisse himself. Now, however, I directed my observation to the Eriksens.

"Your Julenisse is so tiny!" I said.

"No, he is not tiny," said Berit. "He is the proper size for a Julenisse."

"But our American Santa is a large, stout man," I told her.

"Well," Berit responded, "isn't your Santa a sort of duplicate of a true man, a saint from Asia Minor?"

I agreed that this was so.

"But our Julenisse is his very own self, copied from nobody. And his very name tells us that he should be small. Jul means Christmas, and nisse means goblin. Do you see?"

I did. I turned my attention to the Eriksen home.

I have never seen a tidier house. Surely the Eriksens had worked hard and long to have everything so clean and bright. The pots and pans and all the brass and copper had been shined and scrubbed and polished and the wooden kitchen floor was so well scrubbed that it was nearly white.

There in the living room was a Christmas tree which looked quite like our own Christmas trees back home. The decorations were much the same as ours, but the garlands of tiny electric lights strung through the tree were not multicolored. They were plain white. I asked why this was so.

Ødd smiled. "The lights represent the light of candles," he said in good humor. "Hence, they are the color of candle light, and not of gold and red and green and blue and pink and many others. Oh, I have seen colored pictures of American

23

Christmas trees, and always I smile at the different colors which are supposed to be that of the candle."

The family laughed merrily, and I joined them. It seemed the polite thing to do. Besides, I did not ever know, nor even think, that the tree lights were meant to represent candlelight. But in Norway they do, and almost nobody would think of decorating a tree with any lights except those which represent candles.

"We would sooner go hunting at Christmastime," Ødd said. And I guessed that the Norwegian's unusual consideration for the animals and birds at Christmastime precluded the act of harming them during the holy season. Later, the Julenisse told me that I had surmised correctly.

The tree bore pretty animal cookies, gilded nuts, gingerbread figures, red apples and eggshell toys with colored pictures of the Julenisse painted on them.

On the Julebord (Yule table) was a steaming dish of lutefisk or Christmas codfish, which had been dried slowly to give it a strong flavor, then soaked in a lye solution until it became a jellylike mass. There were fancy gingerbreads and animal cookies and some fiske kaker, a sort of fish cake hamburger.

Hjordis gave me the recipe: One pound of boiled fish, two boiled potatoes, one cup of bread crumbs, and pepper and salt to taste.

"Grind together the fish and potatoes," she said, "then mix in the other ingredients. Make small patties and fry them in a pan, just as you do hamburgers. Serve with brown sauce or butter. Then drop some fried onions on top of the cakes and you have fiske kaker."

Hjordis had prepared pickled tongue which was in a place of honor at the table's center, and there was a Christmas message printed on its surface in red vegetable color. It read: "God Jul!"

24

There were remarkable numbers of hot and cold appetizers, ribbestock (pork ribs), cakes and sweets, with risengrynsgrøt served as a dessert. But there was also a small game to be played.

The custom, usually saved for Christmas Day, is sometimes observed on Julaften also. Fru Eriksen always places a single almond into the risengrynsgrøt, ladles the steaming porridge out into bowls and waits to see who will find the almond.

This time Berit was the fortunate one. The almond was in her bowl and her luck brought shouts of happiness from her and groans of make-believe dismay from her family. The person who finds the almond is sure to have good luck during the coming year. Berit, always jolly and optimistic, was certain that the charm of the almond had practical values. She began to think of the things her year of good luck would bring her.

When we had finished the Julaften dinner, we gathered around the fireplace. Because Hjordis is a widow, I was asked to read the Christmas story from the big black family Bible which has been in the Eriksen family for at least three generations. Papa Eriksen had always read the Christmas story to his family but since his death five years ago, Hjordis, then Ødd, had done the reading. This night it was to be their American visitor. The Norwegian words came easily to my lips. At least nobody laughed at my efforts or my accent.

Then came the presents, all placed there beforehand in pretty packages, supposedly by the Julenisse. The children, somewhat beyond the age for toys, received skis and skiing equipment, clothing and books for school. Hjordis was given a small wristwatch, a housecoat, three books and a pair of warm mittens.

The jolly family surprised and pleased me with a gift, too, though they protested it had came through the kindness of the Julenisse, the Christmas gnome. It was a pair of bedroom slippers with sharply curled up toes. The slippers had been made of caribou hide and fashioned by the skilled hands of a Laplander. There are about 30,000 Lapps living in the north of Norway.

After the gift giving, Hjordis and the children joined hands and walked about the tree singing their most loved Christmas carols. Then, at last, silently, awed by the rites of beautiful and ancient traditions, we went softly to bed.

Christmas morning was the time for church. Prest (Pastor) Arnulf Hamsun spoke on the true meaning of Christmas, a message which, I suppose, was echoing from most of the pulpits in the Christian world this day.

At home and at lunch, we dined on the traditional mølje, a piping hot broth in which Christmas meats are cooked. Hjordis served it with flatbrød, a Norwegian bread which is paper thin and crisply delicious. Each of us dipped our flatbrød into the broth which was placed on the kitchen table in the kettle in which it was cooked.

Hjordis seemed to take special pride in her Christmas dish, rulle polse, a tasty, rolled sausage made of pork, veal and beef. It was spiced and brined, then wrapped, boiled and pressed for days. Hjordis served it cold in tidy, thin slices.

Hjordis also served some pleasant-tasting fried cakes which the family laughingly called fattigmands bakkelse (poor man's cakes).

It appeared that the remainder of the day was to be spent quietly, with the youngsters testing their new skis on nearby hills. The Julenisse came to my side invisibly and said that it was time to return. He had, he told me, a worrisome agreement with his fellow Scandinavian Christmas people. We should get back as soon as possible, he said, or there would be trouble. He couldn't know how much! Hjordis and the children, however, bade me stay one more day to observe the

26

Annen Juledag, or Second Christmas day, which is a time for parties. The factories and other places of business customarily hold parties for their employees. Civic organizations have parties, too, for both children and adults.

The Annen Juledag, sometimes called St. Stephen's Day, is also a day when rural folk celebrate with such intensity that they do not, that night, go to bed. Every passerby, no matter who, must stop at every farmhouse along his way, to visit and to partake of food and drink.

I would have liked to visit these country people and to join them in this wonderfully hospitable custom. But the Julenisse insisted that it was time to depart. And, because I was his guest in his country, I agreed.

The moment of return was precisely that, a moment. Almost before I had reluctantly consented to return home, I found myself alone in the backyard of my home next to the Transvolo Stone.

5

CHRISTMAS IN SWEDEN

HEN I made my request at the Transvolo Stone that evening I did so with much humility. I was a supplicant and a very careful one at that. In my last oratory over the Transvolo Stone I had erred by seeming to prefer one Scandinavian country over another. But I did not mean to leave that impression. And now I was most anxious to make friends and to visit anyone, or all, in whatever order seemed best to them. Hence I chose my words very carefully when I addressed my incantation and request to the Transvolo Stone.

When I finished, I made a huge bowl of risengrynsgrøt and placed it on the Transvolo Stone. Then I returned to the house and was full of hope for the tomorrow to come. I slept restlessly.

When morning came I glanced again from my window into the backyard. The risengrynsgrøt bowl was empty but the neighbor's cat was there looking contented. I now knew, I thought, why the little attic people of Scandinavia are said to be invisible to every family member except the cat. I presume that the cat was awake all night and managed to talk the gnomes out of their porridge, and became well fed by doing so.

Also on the Transvolo Stone was a heap of straw which had been piled there, I noted, somewhat in the shape of a human being. I finished breakfast and hurried out to study what might have happened.

Before I reached the Stone, a very sweet, very small voice called out, "Glad Yul!"

Quickly, in a sort of small panic, I searched my memory for some kind of knowledge which might tell me which language this was — not Norwegian, I knew. Finnish? No, the Finns say, "Iloista Joulua." Danish? No, I recall, the Danes say, "Glaedelig Jul."

Since I had spent some time in Norway — when was it? — I knew that the Norwegians say "God Jul" (Good Christmas) or "Gledelig Jul" (Joyous Christmas). So I guessed that the voice was that of a representative of Sweden. But from whom did it come?

As I reached the Transvolo Stone, I called out, "Glad Jul!" This greeting which is used in both Norway and Sweden translates directly to "Glad Christmas," but most simply reckon it to mean "Merry Christmas." (At any rate, I hoped that this would *be* one, without international complications.)

"Takk!" said the sweet voice, and once more I knew that I was being given the extraordinary gift of understanding a foreign language of which, heretofore, I had no knowledge. I saw immediately that the word "thank you" had come from the misshapen clump of straw.

Now that I was near, I could see that the straw was indeed in the image of a person, this one a young lady. She had a small, pretty, wooden face and she was wearing a pleasant, painted smile. Her eyes were blue and seemed to twinkle, and her hair which hung loosely braided down her back was made of the same golden straw which was the material of her construction. Her arms and her waist were tied off, as were her wrists. Her gown was long enough to touch the ground. I could see no feet for she stood directly upon the bottom of her long straw skirt. A hand-made maiden.

"Well, young lady, who are you?" I said it as politely as ever I could. I wished to hurt no more Scandinavian feelings.

29

"I'm a Jul-Dokka," she said, her smile pleasant but fixed.

"A Christmas doll?"

"Yes. This is my first journey abroad."

"It is very nice of you to come," I told her, and I meant it. But I wondered why she had been sent instead of the Jultom-

ten. Was I being punished for previous bad manners by a visit from a less important emissary? I did not dare to ask.

"You would like a visit to Sweden?" she asked. And (pointedly I thought) she added, "With me?"

"Yes, indeed," I replied courteously. Then with sly intent I turned a hint into a question. "How is the Jultomten these days?"

"He is well. But he is so busy during this season, as you can imagine."

"Yes, I am sure he is. When you see him I hope you will tell him that I wish him good health and a very, very long life. And tell him, please, that I think it is very kind of him to send you here as my guide after I have been so thoughtless."

"I will tell him these things," she said, still with her smile which remained constant and unchanging. "But he will be amused when I tell him that you wish him a long life. He is already many hundreds of years old. The Jultomten, you see, is one of many and they are all very, very old people. Each Swedish family has at least one, always invisible but always there. On the old farms in my country, where the same family has lived for many generations, it is thought that the Jultomten is really a sort of collective ghost-goblin made up of the spirits of all the ancestors who lived in the house. Jultomtar live forever."

"Is he also the gift giver in the various families?"

"Oh, yes. But we will be there in time to observe the Christmas joy."

Because of the way time is changed by use of the Transvolo Stone I was never sure of the date on which I was to arrive in the countries I was visiting. I asked.

"Today's date does not matter," she pointed out. "But we will arrive in Sweden on Luciadagen which is December 13."

"That is very early!"

"Yes, Christmas season always begins in Sweden on St. Lucy's Day. I am sure you will be happy to observe our customs."

"I certainly will. And I will be most happy to have you as my friend and guide. You are made of straw, are you not? Is there a reason for this?" I asked the question with great deference to the small lady who, when standing, was barely 18 inches tall.

The story she told me was a pretty one, and very old.

To the early Swedish users of the soil, food was of great importance, for it was not easily obtained in sufficient quantities. Hence every meal was important to these early people. And when, at the end of the growing season the grain was brought in, there was a kind of happy awe over a good crop.

31

But always important was the last bite of food, the Jul-Dokka explained.

It became the custom to make some ceremony over the last sheaf of grain to be brought in from the fields. Hence the early people of the north made a small figurine — a little doll, or Dokka — of the straw and the grain which remained.

As time went on, the custom grew. Dolls were fashioned and sometimes, when all was well, they were placed upon a pole or in a tree so that the wild birds could benefit from a little extra food during the wintertime. Sometimes now, they simply hang a sheaf of grain on a pole or in the Christmas tree which, after Christmas, is taken into the yard. Most of the Scandinavian peoples set out Christmas grain for the birds.

The story of the Dokka pleased me very much. I feel sure that the little rite is so pleasant — and also so helpful — that it ought to be adopted by people of other countries. So, in this manner, does Christmas gather unto itself all of the best of customs, even though a few of the bad ones remain in the tradition, as I was to learn.

The practice of showing their devotion for wild birds came from the country people on Sweden's farmlands, but it grew into the cities at an early time. There is evidence that people in the great city of Stockholm were practicing the custom as early as the middle of the 1600's. Today in the large cities it is not easy to find a shock of wheat or rye to hang, but people make the effort. If sheaves cannot be found, the city dwellers still use their discarded Christmas trees by placing them in their yards or gardens or on their porches or wherever they can. They put suet and seeds among the boughs of the Christmas tree.

The Jul-Dokka was, she told me, made of rye straw. I hoped she pardoned me when I made a weak joke. "You do not look a bit seedy to me," I said. (Fortunately her smile was painted on her face.)

We left then. I heard a whooshing sound and, not to my surprise, I found myself strolling down a gravel road in a rural district about five miles outside of the city of Kalmar. The Dokka told me the name. She was riding on my right shoulder. I had discovered she was without feet because walking is not one of her requirements. The day was pleasantly warm and I was surprised that it was.

"This part of Sweden is always surprisingly warm to every visitor," she explained. "The temperature here now is about 35 degrees (your kind of temperature, Fahrenheit), and that is warm for a place in such a northern latitude. In Kalmar, February is the coldest month of the year but the average temperature is only about 27 degrees."

We strolled, or at least I did, past several pleasantly tidy farms but I did not wish to ask where we were going. It is easy to walk along a country road. I noted that the sheaves of grain had already been placed on poles, on trees, and sometimes on the eaves of the houses.

We turned in at a little farmhouse where Jul-Dokka told me to knock at the door. I noticed that she moved well aside. "Swedish people are not accustomed to seeing an ambulatory Jul-Dokka," she explained.

Her move was well timed. At the very second I raised my hand to knock on the wooden door I heard a rumbling sound from above. I looked up just in time to see what must have been hundreds of pounds of snow come cascading down upon me. Then, faintly from beneath the snow, I heard excited voices. People were digging me out and I waited, pressed down and made helpless by the weight of the snow. Above me through the blanket of white, I could see hands at work digging carefully around my face. Then, at last, a patch of blue sky became visible. I was freed from the pinioning avalanche.

My rescuers were members of the Olaus Geijer family. His

wife, Birgitta, was sweeping a homemade broom over me. The two children, 12 year old Gunnar, and Selma, aged 14, were flicking dish towels at me to snap the snow from my clothing. For myself, I was busy trying to reach down the back of my neck where the snow had packed and was making me cold and uncomfortable as it melted.

Olaus looked up toward the roof and shook his fist. When I glanced at him with apparent wonder, he muttered a single word of explanation, "Jultomten!" Then I understood that the "accident" was no accident at all. Tomtens play rough.

In the little farmhouse which smelled pleasantly of spices and wood smoke, my host required me to change clothes and don one of his sets of work clothes which smelled of sweet hay, pipe smoke and goats. There was much talk and many apologies for the avalanche which was apparently my Christmas present from the Jultomten.

It was clear here also that the family was engaged in much pre-Christmas activity. Tomorrow, they told me, was Luciadagen and everything must be in readiness for it. Sweden observes Christmas from the advent of St. Lucy's Day, December 13, through Tjugondag Knut (St. Knut's Day), January 13.

A large pot containing lutefisk sat at the side of the fireplace while over the hot coals there bubbled a potful of mixed pork, sausage and corned beef. Selma cut great slices of wort bread and Mama Birgitta (we would call her Bridget) was tending the lutefisk and burying it deep under beech ashes to make it sweet and tender for Christmas.

Papa Olaus served me a spicy drink of Swedish Christmas glogg which is guaranteed to stir heat in cold muscles. He makes it like this:

Two teaspoons of whole allspice, 4 sticks cinnamon, 1 tablespoon of whole cloves, one gallon of cider, 1-1/3 cups of brown sugar (or honey), two tablespoons of grated lemon peel, and a dash of nutmeg. '

He combined the allspice, the cinnamon, the cloves, the cider, the brown sugar and the grated lemon peel and simmered the mixture gently for 25 minutes. He strained the combination through a fine sieve and served it quickly with a dash of nutmeg and a stick of cinnamon in each glass. Such a recipe, he said, would serve fifteen or twenty people.

I was thoroughly warm after sipping the aromatic, highly flavored glogg and it seemed a good time for Birgitta to call us to table for the traditional meal of dopp i grytan, or "dipping in the kettle."

Before we sat down to the table and before the big kettle of the appetizing broth was placed in its center, Selma walked about the room tossing straw on the floor — a reminder of the birth in the manger. Then the big kettle was placed on the table and we were told to begin. I did not know how to go about it, so, as many a guest has done at many another place, I pretended to be busy as I secretly watched my hosts.

Each of them picked up a slice of the vörtbröd (wort bread), stabbed it with a fork, then dipped the bread into the steaming mixture and ate it, usually with a bit of the sausage or a slice of pork or corned beef.

I presumed that this was our evening meal and therefore dined heartily. I was to learn, however, that it merely preceded the principal course and that the dipping in the kettle was only a ritual for good luck.

When I had finished with the dipping, my host again served me a glass of steaming glogg and also to Birgitta, himself and the tiniest drop to each of the children.

We took turns offering toasts, some of them amusing, and there was much laughter and exchanges of wishes for a God Jul. Then we moved into the next room where there was a

great display of many foods, the wondrous Swedish smorgas-
bord which included ham, roast goose with prune stuffing,
lingonberries cooked in honey, and many preserves which
Birgitta and Selma had put up for the winter.

Olaus explained that they were not dining in the fashion
of the day for St. Lucy, but were having their Christmas
dinner beforehand in my honor.

Olaus added, "We do this because we understand that you
will not be with us at Christmastime." It was news to me.

Then after an embarrassed silence he explained that he had
had warnings from what he called "our little attic man." It
meant, of course, that the Jultomtar of Sweden were all in
favor of oppressing me because they thought I had slighted
them and their country.

But Olaus said that he wished I would stay at least over
St. Lucy's Day. Olaus told me that his family had planned
to have their entire Christmas celebration in the two days
instead of through the traditional seven weeks, all in my honor.
When I protested that I did not wish him to trouble himself
in this manner on my account, he laughed and his family
joined him. They are hospitable people and I could not per-
suade them to change their plans. Now Olaus read the biblical
story of the birth of Christ.

When we had tired, Olaus walked to the closed doors of
the parlor and threw them open wide. Selma and Gunnar
rushed to look in and shouted with glee at the first view they
had had this season of the lighted Christmas tree which, as
always, had been readied secretly by their mother and father.

While they were exulting over its bright and dazzling
beauty, there came a hard knock on the front door, a single
bump. Gunnar hurried to the door and opened it. Two goats
stood there — they called them the Julbockar — and they were
cordially invited into the house. The Julbockar are, in theory,

36

the goats belonging to an ancient thunder god of the pagans.

These, however, belonged to no thunder god at all. They were, in fact, two neighbors of the Geijer family who had been recruited for this special early Christmas in my honor. They were dressed as goats, as if for a costume party. The Julbockar served as the customary sled power for the Christmas Jultomten who was, I was told, waiting outside. I offered to leave the scene but again I was the object of their laughter.

The Jultomten was not the attic gnome this time. It was a standard-sized man dressed much in the manner of our own Santa Claus. He wore a long white beard, a red tunic, red trousers and a tassel cap of knitted red wool. And he carried a large burlap bag containing Christmas presents. He was, in fact, the children's Uncle Frans.

Uncle Frans, the Jultomten for the occasion, wished us a happy holiday before he handed out the presents which included one for me, a lovely little pewter vase of graceful, simple design.

As the members of the family accepted their gifts, I moved into the corner of the room and listened to the fluid, lilting speech of Sweden.

Swedish is classified in the northern branch of the Germanic tongue and is an eastern development of the *Donsk tunga,* or Danish tongue, a name which long ago was applied not only to Danish but to the speech of all Scandinavia. Modern Swedish has an unusual accent which combines musical pitch as well as stress on a syllable to such an extent that not only pronunciation but meaning may depend upon the musical accent of the word used.

But, as Olaus soon told us, it was time for bed. "Luciadagen arrives early in the morning," he said. And it did.

We did not slumber long. Before the slanting sun of the

north had a full opportunity to turn the black night sky into morning grey, Lucy was abroad.

Lucy's Day in Sweden is sometimes referred to as Little Yule. Every parish in Sweden has a "Lucy Bride," and many families have one. In homes where there is a daughter, she is the Lucy Bride. And in homes where there is more than one daughter, the honor always falls to the eldest girl.

St. Lucy is represented as a girl wearing a white dress, a red sash and a crown of lingonberry or whortleberry leaves with white candles which are lighted (and dangerous) and twined in wire placed in her hair.

The Lucy which they commemorate on December 13 was born in Syracuse, Sicily, in about A.D. 283. She is the patroness of Syracuse. She was said to have been so beautiful that she attracted the attention of a heathen nobleman of power and authority. When she rejected his suit for her hand, he caused her to be tortured and her eyes plucked out. In the cathedral at Syracuse, she is depicted as a suffering maiden and is posed with a vessel which contains her eyes. In Italy, Santa Lucia is one of the most honored saints, but she is also the patroness of all who suffer from eye diseases. Some of the legends say that St. Lucy plucked out her own eyes because the heathen prince thought they were so beautiful that he must have her for his wife.

On this blue-dark morning at perhaps 3:30 o'clock, the Lussi or Lussibruden (Lucy Bride) knocked upon my door and then entered, the lighted candles casting a strange light in the room. The light of the candles made it appear to be a halo over her head. In her hands she bore a tray of strong, hot coffee and some little cakes, the lussikatter (Lucy cakes), tasty little buns in the form of a cross. Selma wished me a God Jul and departed.

I finished the hot, strong coffee and the Lucy cakes and hurried downstairs to observe what else must take place on this day. Mam Brigitta had prepared more coffee and some pepparkakor, spicy ginger cookies. The room was lighted by many candles. Selma sat in great dignity and spoke little, though Olaus insisted that she dine with us — and also that her candles be extinguished.

Soon I learned that our Selma was the Lucy Bride for the entire little farm settlement nearby. And presently at our door there were several dozen little boys. They were the stjarngossar, or Star Boys. They also wore white but their heads were capped by tall, silver-colored peaked hats which were decorated with stars and had moons pasted on them. A few of the boys carried Lucy cakes to give to the neighbors.

Luciadagen is a day of many lights, the special mark of the festival. Though I could not think what there was about the story of St. Lucy which required the use of so many lights and candles, the name Lucy or Lucia suggests the Latin word *lux* which means "light." And one remembers that according to the old style calendar, St. Lucy's Day was the shortest day of the year — the turning point in the winter and the promise of lighter days to come.

I walked behind the growing procession as the children visited the homes of the neighbors but I was not to be permitted to take part. In the gleaming darkness, someone snatched my hat from my head and threw it to the ground.

As I bent to retrieve it, I was butted (by a goat?) and knocked down, sprawling. As I tried to hurry away, I was tripped by an unseen person, and as I fled back toward the home of my hosts, I was pelted by snowballs. Very small snowballs, about the size which would be made by very tiny hands like those of the Jultomtar of Sweden. Then, suddenly I found myself sitting on the Transvolo Stone in my backyard, and very happy to be there and unharmed.

6

A SULKY SANTA CLAUS

NOW perceived that there are remarkable sensitivities in the various peoples of the world. Some are painfully provincial or local in their thoughts and beliefs. They are unwilling or unable to accept the beliefs of other peoples. I was determined that I would do nothing further to offend the people of any country. Though I had not intentionally slighted anybody, I knew now that one must approach each country with extreme care. My fault had been ignorance. I decided to make certain to know more about a country before I went for a visit there.

Now, I thought, would be a good time to go to Belgium, a rather small country only about 175 miles long and 90 miles wide. Although it is the most densely populated country in Europe (with about 765 persons to the square mile), it is a place small enough for me to comprehend and to avoid stepping on international toes.

I decided to borrow some wisdom and good judgment. I stood on the Transvolo Stone and called for our own Santa Claus. Then I went into the house to await his arrival. Previously my visitors, when beckoned, always came more slowly than when we whisked ourselves to other countries. I never knew why, but I thought perhaps they might have to pass through American customs.

I was awakened next morning by the sound of jingling bells and I knew that Santa Claus had accepted my invitation. I dressed and went out to visit with him.

"Merry Christmas," he said in dolorous tones.

"Merry Christmas to you, Santa," I replied enthusiastically, trying to show amiability despite his dour manner.

"You called?"

"Yes, Santa. I have some problems that I thought you might be willing to help me solve. I seem to have fallen into the unintentional habit of offending visitors from other countries. I can't help it, but I just seem to do the wrong things. Do you have a little time to help me get straightened out? Everyone is so sensitive," I complained.

"Well," he said slowly, "I am really quite busy these days. I do not have very much time for anything but my problems here."

Santa stressed the word "here" and I guessed at the reasons for his restraint. Was he, too, being jealous and provincial?

"Santa, I thought you were the proper one to help me in my associations with other peoples. You will agree that we should be able to get along well with the nations of the world, won't you?"

Stiffly, he said, "I have my world and they seem to want theirs."

"But Santa," I replied, "you and I — we're Americans. And we ought to try to work together in the interests of international harmony."

"But I'm not really an American. I came here from The Netherlands and I am more properly Dutch or, at least, of Dutch descent. The Netherlands should be my territory, too."

"Santa Claus!" I said it with surprise in my voice, and I did it purposely. "You are as American as I am! And my family has been here only two generations. You arrived here long before I did."

"Well . . ."

"Yes, Santa, you are quite American. All of us came here from other countries, or at least our ancestors did. We call ourselves Americans and properly so. We feel American, we act American, and we think American. Every one of us is American."

"I have heard it said that only the American Indians are true Americans," Santa replied, still rigid with reserve.

"I have heard it, too. But even the Indians immigrated here. If we take your point of view, there is no such person as an American."

"No. Only Indians are true Americans," he said.

Santa was being petulant because, I suppose, I had been hobnobbing with the Christmas people of other lands and even bringing them here to the domain of Santa Claus. He was being stubborn. He was being wrong, too.

Most archaeologists today agree that the people we erroneously call "Indians" began to occupy the New World between 10,000 and 40,000 years ago. They came here from their homes in northeastern Asia. Over the course of many centuries, these peoples moved in search of animal herds onto the great central plain of Alaska out of Siberia. In those distant days when the geology of the earth was somewhat different from the land today, there was a land bridge, a natural one, which led from Siberia into Alaska, then south and east through an open lane or corridor which ran by the eastern slopes of the Rocky mountains. When they came here they came to a land which contained no other human beings. Then, over the centuries they continued to come from various parts of Asia, through Siberia, into Alaska and what is now the United States. By the time white men came, the Indians were occupying the entire hemisphere.

So the Indians migrated here too. I told Santa Claus this. Reluctantly he said that it sounded correct — as far as it went.

"Then you won't help me?" I asked.

"Well, it does seem to me that when you invite Christmas people from other countries, you might at least ask my permission to bring them to the land which I have served by myself for several hundreds of years."

"I am sorry I didn't ask you. But I'm asking you now to help me make friends with other peoples who represent the Christmas festival. Will you please?"

Santa's eyes flashed.

"Why should I? They — these other people — they don't help *me*! They oppose me, and they fight against the tradition which I represent. I don't see why you come to me for help. I am offended by the way those people act toward me."

I asked for an explanation. I got a fierce one.

"Look at Spain for example," Santa Claus said. His ruddy cheeks seemed brighter red than before. "Look at Spain," he repeated. "You know what Spain did in 1950? They *banned* the use of the word 'Christmas' because it is an English word. The reason they did it was because the Catholic clergy in Spain think of Christmas folk customs and Santa Claus as being essentially Protestant."

I couldn't have stopped Santa's soliloquy if I wanted to. He seemed almost to be talking to encourage himself into staying angry. He went on.

"Look at what Hungary has done! Starting in 1951, Hungary held a campaign to discredit me. They took the so-called 'communist line' and they began to criticize me, to laugh at me and to deride me. They called me a 'tool of American capitalists!'

"And look at South Africa. In that place, they denounce me and refuse to let me serve their children. One of the cultural organizations in South Africa not only refused to let me into the country but they called me 'a foreign importation which is unsuited to the ideals of Afrikaners.' Do you think I have to take that and then try to help *them*?"

He really was angry! He hurried on.

"Russia. Look at Russia! They laugh at me. They deride me, call me names, make fun of me. They get their Christmas presents not from Santa Claus but from a grandpa, or a raggedy old woman whom they call Grandma Babushka. And they simply don't BELIEVE in Christmas!

"And France. Look at France! Every few years somebody in the clergy of that country gets suspicious of my motives and attacks me. They oppose me because they say I'm 'just American.' And the French Canadians have been unkind to me — hostile and aggressive. One year it was so terrible — the way they attacked me and called me names — that I wouldn't even try to deliver toys to the children in the French Canadian areas, like Quebec. And believe me, I had a lot of toys left over that year! It was 1947, I think. Oh, I had a lot of extra toys. You know what the French Canadians called me that year? 'A neo-pagan custom!' Now, answer me. What is a neo-pagan custom? Is it a nice term? I do not think it is."

I explained that I thought it meant something new fangled, made up or spun out of an old pagan belief.

"See!" he shouted as if he knew all the time that it was un-complimentary. I could easily guess that the term "neo-pagan custom" had been disturbing Santa ever since he had first heard it back in 1947.

"And the French people . . . they have no respect for me at all. Do you think that I am the one allowed to bring gifts to their children? No, they use an imposter named Père Noël and never even let their children send *me* a letter. So I can't go there, but you . . . you sit on your Transvolo Stone and blithely invite every one of those people over here into my territory. And you ask me to help you get more of them here and also to help you keep *them* from being offended. Offended? What about *me*? Who cares if I'm offended? Nobody, that's who."

It was a very long speech. Never once did Santa Claus say, "Ho Ho Ho" although I had always thought that was a principal part of his vocabulary. But today he didn't think he had cause for levity.

Santa had apparently been brooding over these slights, some serious and some minor, but all magnified by his sensitive thoughts. He had, he said, always tried to do the right thing and hence it was difficult for him to know that he was being criticized and attacked through no fault of his own.

It took a great deal of skillful persuasion for me to get some advice from Santa Claus. And it was some advice he finally gave me. Some advice!

I explained that I wanted to go to Belgium and that I hoped I had his permission to invite the Belgian Christmas people here to my backyard. I promised him that I would permit no alien

Christmas personage to deliver packages, toys, gifts or any other form of holiday greeting to anybody beyond the borders of my backyard. He insisted that I write it down on paper and sign it.

"Do as you would be done by," said Santa Claus rather smugly, I thought.

"Santa," I said, "if you don't mind my saying so, I think that is an unkind thing to say. In fact, you are misquoting and misusing the Golden Rule."

After several hours of discussion wherein I used cajolery, sweet talk, persuasion and good humor, Santa Claus said he would be more lenient in his attitudes toward people of the world who do not believe in him.

"Maybe," I said, "some day Santa will be a *world* figure."

The thought pleased him. He said he was aware of the fact that Japan had adopted the Santa Claus custom and the outward appearance of the Christmas festival even though Japan is not a Christian country.

It does seem strange that in a nation like Japan whose principal religions are Buddhism and Shinto there is any recognition of Christmas. Yet Japan pays great attention to this Christian festival, though with no religious overtones whatsoever.

The Japanese call Christmas "Kurimasu" and they practice it only as a matter of commerce. The Japanese are among the world's finest businessmen. They have done much to make Kurimasu a great festival — for spending money. But on the days before Kurimasu there is great activity on the streets and the shopping areas of the cities. Christmas trees are lighted and placed about the streets and in the stores just as they are in our country. Toys are used to decorate the branches. There is a spirit of happiness and joy on the streets as the shoppers wend their way in search of gifts for loved ones.

But Santa Claus is there, too.

In China, also, there is a semblance of Christmas as we know it, especially among the Christian Chinese. But the Christian Chinese are greatly outnumbered by the three principal religions, Buddhism, Taoism and Confucianism. Christmas is called Sheng Dan Jieh (Festival of the Holy Birth) and the Christmas tree in China is known as the Tree of Light. These trees are decorated handsomely with brightly colored paper ornaments in the form of flowers, paper chains in colors of green, red, yellow and blue, and imitation snowflakes formed of cotton balls.

When I jokingly told Santa Claus that he might try to look a bit more Oriental so that he might serve the children in the Far East too, he laughed and squinted up his eyes. He did not look very convincing but I could tell what was in his mind. I was ashamed of him.

I confess I felt somewhat sorry for Santa. He had tried to be a good and a generous person and he had been shunted about by people who have their own gift giver and who see no reason to change.

But at one point in our conversation, Santa said that even in the United States there were people who were, he said, "trying to depose or adjust" him.

He called my attention to a Methodist minister of Millbrae, California, who advocates the transfer of the gift giving custom of Christmastime to Thanksgiving. The minister wants to change the name of Thanksgiving day to "Thanksmas" and, if he has his way, Thanksmas will include what he calls "stomach stuffing and gift giving rituals." Then, he says, this will leave Christmas unsullied by commercialism, observed only as a strictly religious time.

Santa said, "The minister may have good intentions. But he doesn't think of me and my work. Getting all the toys and gifts made as early as November is almost impossible. As it is," he said petulantly, "I am working almost up to the very limit of time allotted to me on Christmas eve. No, I couldn't finish my work in time to deliver them by Thanksgiving. The idea is preposterous. I just can't do it, that's all."

He was becoming angry again so I hurried to soothe his feelings. But he had already begun.

"My troubles aren't always with outsiders," he said, grieving. "Even here in the United States, along with Minister What's-His-Name in California, there are people who don't care for me and my work. Some of the ethnic or cultural groups resist me or attempt to.

"I've been resisted by the Pennsylvania Germans, the Latin Americans, the Greeks and even some of the Scandinavians. They want their own kind of festival and it doesn't seem to include poor old Santa," he said. I thought I saw tears in his eyes but I was not certain.

But at long last Santa agreed to advise, to the best of his ability and "in the interest of relieving world tensions." Those were his very words.

About Belgium, he said, I need have no worries. But, he said, perhaps I would make friends more quickly and surely if I used the correct name of Belgium when I called for a visitor from there.

"What do you mean, the correct name?" I asked.

"Well," he said pompously, "we Americans do not use the precisely proper name for other countries."

"What should we call it?"

"Call it what they themselves call it," Santa advised. "And that is Belgie. So when you make your magic incantation and specify the country you hope to visit, you would be wise to flatter the country by using its own name."

"A capital suggestion, Santa Claus," I said. "I was sure you would be willing to help me."

That is what I said then. I know now that Santa Claus had

bamboozled me and tricked me into creating an incident which I would like to forget and which I think Belgium would like to forget, too. International relations hang in precarious balance because the people of the world do not always understand each other and do not try to. Even Christmas people!

7

BELGIUM, BELGIQUE, BELGIE

N ALL innocence (and ignorance) I performed the magic rites, uttered the required incantation and added my wish to be transported to — I said it proudly and distinctly — "Belgie" in time for their "Kerstdag" — their Christmas. Almost instantly I was smitten across the flat of the stomach by a long staff. A small, black faced person appeared instantly and struck me. I did not recognize him. Two things I knew immediately: the small man wore a long cloak and a strange hat, and he knew how to swing a pike pole. I doubled up, out of breath and gasping for air. The pain was minimal, but the shock of being attacked so swiftly and without provocation was almost more than I could bear.

I slumped to my knees and rested, waiting for I do not know what. But my assailant had disappeared. The long pole he had used to strike me was lying there across the Transvolo Stone where he had dropped it. After kneeling there motionless for 10 uneventful minutes, I picked up the staff and moved slowly to my house to rest and to ponder. What had I done wrong this time?

I examined the long pole which my adversary had left behind. It was tough and worn smooth by handling over a long period of time. Strangely, it smelled of vinegar. I studied it to seek some clue which might tell me whom I had offended and how I had done so. I reckoned, too, that I was now to be excluded from Belgium as I was, apparently, from Finland and Denmark. What tribulations there are for the innocent (and ignorant) emissary!

I chanced to glance out of the window as I brooded. I was surprised to see two persons sitting back to back on the Trans-volo Stone. They were not engaged in conversation. Their manner did not suggest congeniality. I picked the stick from the floor where I had placed it and was about to set it in the closet. But I glanced out of the window again for a better look at my two guests. One of them was a small person with a black face, a long cloak and a strange hat. He was the small black man who had struck me less than an hour earlier. I elected to take the pole with me. Nothing, I reasoned, is wrong with being prepared to defend one's self, even from one's guests.

The other guest looked very much like a high priest. Though the distance from the house to the Transvolo Stone is a hundred yards, I could see him well enough to think he might be a bishop of some church or other. I walked out to the Stone as casually as I could, but I held the staff in my right hand, ready for whatever kind of greeting I might get.

"Merry Christmas," I said directing the greeting to both persons but intending it for only one.

"Merry Christmas," said the taller man. His voice was pleasant and his speech was Flemish. He was wearing a bishop's mitre which is a tall, oddly shaped liturgical headdress worn by bishops and abbots as a symbol of office. He also wore the long robe of a bishop, and he carried a pastoral staff similar to the one which had been used to hit me across the stomach.

The small black man did not speak at once. He, too, wore a long robe and an unusual hat which came to a point at the top. His face reflected anger or pique, I did not know which, but his eyes were bright and his attitude suggested wisdom and intelligence. However, there was no question about one thing: He was very, very angry.

I introduced myself and made it clear that I was doing so to both guests.

The bishop nodded and acknowledged the introduction.

"I am Sinterklaas," he said. He seemed to wait for the small blackamoor to introduce himself, but he did not do so. Then, nodding politely toward the sitting Moor, the bishop said, "And this, I believe, is Père Fouettard who comes from the southern parts of Belgium. He is the assistant of the Sinterklaas there."

Now the little black man bridled, refreshing his anger from what Sinterklaas had said. He spoke then, quickly (and surprisingly to me) in Spanish accents.

"I am not the assistant to Sinterklaas," he said. "I am the helper of Père Noël. And I am not from Belgium, nor am I from Belgie. I am from the proud kingdom of Belgique."

53

I now had a glimmering of what I had done wrong, but I was not yet certain. I bowed politely to the little man.

"I am delighted to have you as my guest," I said. "And I would like very much to visit you in . . . in Belgique . . . during the Christmas festival."

I was surprised to find that now Sinterklaas became angry. His head snapped back and the glistening mitre on his head trembled. He spoke sharply.

"It is properly called Belgie," he said.

"Excuse me," I told them both. "I meant Belgie. I would enjoy visiting there during Christmas Eve."

"No. It is *Belgique,*" said the dark-faced man. "And it is not called Christmas Eve. It is La Veille De Saint Nicolas."

"Pardon me," said the bishop figure. "It is *properly* called Sint Nikolaas Vooravond. This, of course, depends upon whether one wishes to speak properly. And to speak properly where I come from in Belgie is to speak Flemish."

"Walloon!" said the black man. "Only this is proper!"

I fully comprehended now. Belgium is a land with no language of its own. Hence it must speak another. By the vicissitudes of history and geography, it has, unfortunately, two languages. I made a soft promise to myself that I would have a few words with our American Santa Claus for getting me into this trouble. I was sure that he planned this unpleasant development.

"Well," I said, still addressing the two people, "I am pleased you have both come."

"I came only to retrieve my staff," said Père Fouettard. "Then I return."

"I have your staff here, Père Fouettard," I told him, "but I will not return it to you if you have any intention of using it. I think I might tell you now, that was a very unsociable thing you did to me when I invited you here."

54

"You did not invite me," he railed, his voice in a high pitch. "You said you wanted to go to Belgie. I live in Belgique. You deserved to be punished for your insult to southern Belgique."

"I do not think you have the privilege of coming into a strange land and punishing an absolute stranger just because he does not speak your language. Who gives you such authority to punish people?"

Sinterklaas answered for him. "Père Fouettard is the father of the spanking. It is his duty in . . . in the place he comes from to punish naughty children when they deserve it. He dips his rod or stick in vinegar, then flays the little ones."

"But he did not spank me. He hit me across the stomach. I did not deserve it."

"It *was* deserved," said the small black man. "I am the helper of Père Noël — not Sint Nikolaas or Sinterklass, as uneducated persons might speak the name in the vernacular. And, as his helper, I am committed to the duty of punishing wrongdoers. Give me my staff."

"You may not have it until you promise not to use it, either here or on any innocent child," I said. I did not like his aggressive attitude nor his manner of showing authority.

"If a child does not know his catechism, he is not innocent and he must be punished," the black man said. "If he is otherwise naughty or stupid, he must also be punished."

I turned to Sinterklaas. "Is this true everywhere in your country?"

"Yes, it is the custom. Where I live, my helper is Zwarte Piet. He inflicts the spankings."

"Zwarte Piet — does that translate to Black Pete?"

"Ja."

"Then your helper — he is also black of color?"

"Ja."

Now I turned to Père Fouettard, father of spankings. "Is Zwarte Piet in your likeness? Does he look somewhat like you?"

"Oui. But we do not speak together."

"Are you Spanish?"

"Si."

"And Zwarte Piet?"

"Also Spanish."

"But you do not speak to each other?"

"Non."

"Does this strike you as being a sensible arrangement?"

"Very," he said with a note of insolent assurance.

I turned to the bishop. "Does it seem sensible to you?"

He sighed. "Our country has problems, very serious problems which tend to cause quarrels among the people. It is made up fundamentally of two distinctly different ethnic groups. The Flemings are of Teutonic origin. Like their Dutch neighbors over the northern border, they are fair haired, blue eyed and fair complexioned and they speak the language of the Dutch.

"The Walloons, though, are of Celtic origin. They live mainly in the southern parts of our country, and they resemble the dark haired French who live across the southern and western borders. The Walloons speak a French patois, a somewhat old form of the French language which is called Walloon. The problems there are based largely upon the two languages of the country."

"Are the Flemish and Walloons about equal in numbers?"

"No. The Flemings are in the majority by a ratio of about four Flemings to three Walloons, with each people living among their own kind as a general thing. The provinces which are predominantly Flemish are Antwerp, West Flanders, East Flanders and Limburg. Walloon country, where majorities are French speaking, is generally comprised of Hainaut, Liège, Luxembourg and Namur."

56

I asked about the religions. "You are undoubtedly of the Catholic faith, Sinterklaas?"

"Yes. Most people in our country are Catholic."

"The greatest problem," he added, "is one of paramount concern — the linguistic controversies which continually disturb our happiness."

"But these problems — they should not involve the Christmas festival, should they?"

"Oui!" said Père Fouettard sharply, "They should! The people of our country should speak properly, and that means they should speak Walloon."

" But I do not agree," said Sinterklaas.

"And I do not agree with either of you," I said quickly. "The world is too small for controversy. And controversy within a single country like yours seems foolish."

The small black man looked into my eyes and snorted. I knew what he meant. My own country is no stranger to controversy, either.

"Give me my stick," he said.

"Do you promise not to use it on me or on innocent children?"

He nodded. I handed it to him and he rose to go.

"Are you not going to invite me to your beautiful country?" I asked the question in plaintive tones.

"Not if you choose to go to the Flemish segments of my country," he said. Then he disappeared by fading slowly away, his tough stick being the last to go.

I directed my question to Sint Nikolaas. "Are *you* going to invite me to *your* beautiful country?"

He shook his head. "It would mean only trouble. Père Fouettard would punish you severely."

"But he promised not to use the stick on me or on innocent children, and I hope he will keep that promise."

"Père Fouettard's entire purpose in life is to punish. And he believes that when he punishes a child he will not think the child innocent. And thus he does not break his promise to you. Any child who does not know the catechism is guilty of wrong."

"But I may not visit Belgie?"

"The trouble would be too great."

I could not help but express my disappointment, but the bearded one was not to have his mind changed. However, he said that he would try to describe for me the Christmas of his country.

"Why," I asked, "is the helper of Sint Nikolaas a person of Spanish descent?"

He explained. "It is a distant reason. A political situation as far back as the 1400's gave part of what is now Belgium to Charles, the heir to the Spanish throne. When Charles ascended the throne of Spain, the Netherlands became part of the Spanish dominions. When the son of Charles, Philip the Second, ruled the land despotically, the people rose in revolt. The southern provinces (Belgium) remained loyal to the Roman Catholic Church and hence to the Spanish crown; and the northern provinces, which were a stronghold of Protestantism, won their independence as The Netherlands. When Spain lost parts of Belgium to France many years later, many things remained, including the custom of Père Fouettard as well as Black Peter.

"But," he continued, "Christmas in Belgium is not the day of gift giving. For children it is not December 25th which is important, but December 6th. That's my day," the saint said proudly.

"Your day?"

"Yes. The day of Sinterklaas."

He explained that on Sint Nikolaas Vooravond, which is

St. Nicholas Eve, the saint himself rides a gray donkey or — depending upon the region — a white horse. On this important day, December 5, he is unseen although he himself sees everything. He visits every home where there are children. He picks up the carrots and the bits of bread which the children have placed for him in chimney corners. They know he will be hungry from his long journey.

Sometime during the evening, as the children sing songs to the patron saint, a door pops open and many candies are tossed into the room. They have been thrown by an unseen but well known person. By the time every bit of candy has been picked up, Sinterklaas has departed. The children hurry to bed to await the morning of December 6, the proper day for gift giving. They have, of course, left their shoes near the chimney for the old saint to stuff with good things and special treats — an orange, perhaps, or pieces of marzipan candy, or flat little cakes called klaasjes or pieces of speculaus, a spicy, hard gingerbread which has been molded into the shape of Sinterklaas himself. Then, when the shoes are filled with good things, other presents are strewn nearby — clothing, knitted hats or scarves or beautiful warm mittens which somebody skillful, like grossmutter, or grandmother, has knitted for the great day and loved ones.

The children of Belgium use their shoes as the receptacles of most of the gifts because it is tradition but also because they have not discovered, as American and English children have, that stockings hold more — they *stretch*.

Christmas (Kerstdag) is principally a time for religious observations, though on the eve of Christmas there are family celebrations held after midnight Mass. Then they tell ghost stories and sing ballads while the elders drink heady brews. So said the bishop.

At last, when the eldest children go to bed, somebody like

the Angel Gabriel, or even the Child Jesus, will somehow find time to come to the house and place a slice of engelskoek (angel's cake) beneath the pillows of all good boys and girls.

Indeed, said Sinterklaas, Christmas in Belgium goes on outside of the homes as well as inside. Great bells ring from the church steeples, sounding out 99 tolls. People everywhere go into the street and wind their way about the town in a long, slow, beautiful procession. Bands play and children sing and priests chant, and they move thus to their churches.

On Christmas day throughout Flanders, each of the church congregations presents its own Christmas play, an important social and dramatic event which is taken with great seriousness. The play is usually the same from year to year, but as the decades fly past, small changes born of the whims of the actors find their way into the dialogue and the action and — as it is safe to guess — the play presented in 1870 is different indeed from the play presented in 1970, although it is intended to be the same. The stories are religious — the simple sweet one of the birth of Christ, or the story of the shepherds and their part on the holy day.

In each Belgian village also, according to the bishop, three local men are elected to serve as the three wise men, but those selected for the parts must be deserving indeed; being one of the Magi is a great honor which all men would be proud to have. They dress in appropriate robes and visit each home in their parish or village. There they stand and sing two songs — one song describing the travels of the Magi, and the other, the German song "O Tannenbaum" sung in Flemish. The men acting the parts of the Magi are always invited in for tea and pancakes, according to the old tradition; and never are three men more surfeited with food than are these actors of the holy scene in the lovely country where traditions do not die.

But the Christmas season is not yet over. On December 28th comes the strange festival called Allerkindereng or Holy Innocents' Day. It is supposed to be a recollection of the anniversary of the slaughter of the children of Bethlehem by Herod who sought by such murders to kill the Infant Jesus.

Sinterklaas paused in his telling to point out that there is a legend in Belgium that once, ever so long ago, the bodies of two of these murdered young ones were found in the church of St. Gerard in the province of Namur. But, the old saint pointed out, Holy Innocents' Day is — strangely enough — not a day for melancholy, but a day for fun. On this day children are traditionally allowed to play tricks upon their parents and all elders. One favorite, frequent jest is locking one's parent in a room where he has gone unsuspectingly. He is not given his freedom unless he pays a ransom demanded by the children. The imprisoned person, whoever he may be, is never called by his true relationship, such as mother or father, but as the "sugar aunt" or "sugar uncle," perhaps because the ransom is usually something sweet.

The Christmas tree, all dressed in pretty candies or cookies and other ornaments, is like most Christmas trees of most countries.

The voice of the old bishop droned on and on. As I looked into the sky at the gathering darkness, I realized that we had been visiting all the day. His speech came more slowly and then it ceased altogether. I looked at the old saint and saw that at last he had fallen asleep. I did not know if I should be so bold as to wake him or let the adventure take its own course. But the matter was settled for me presently. I, too, fell asleep. I dreamed of new troubles abroad. Sometimes dreams come true. Mine did.

8

CHRISTMAS CAROLS

WHEN I next visited the Transvolo Stone, I asked for nothing more than a visit from Santa Claus. He came almost immediately but with a certain amount of reluctance. And well he should.

"Santa," I admonished him. "I am surprised at your behavior. I think that you purposely misled me and caused me much embarrassment and difficulty."

I rubbed my hand across my stomach and added, "And a terrific smash across the stomach."

He stroked his white beard, saying nothing. I was sure it would cause him distress to be obliged to admit the duplicity he had been guilty of. Nevertheless I was determined that he must help me on my next adventure. I wished to make him contrite before I asked advice from him. I did not want another experience such as I had had from the visitors from Belgium.

"Have you nothing to say, Santa? You purposely caused trouble."

"I was protecting my interests against an invasion of foreign powers." He said it shortly, with an edge in his voice. He was being protective indeed.

"It was not nice," I protested. "It was a bad thing to do to a fellow American."

"Very well," he said. "Perhaps it was not the noblest of actions. But don't you see that we have enough foreign imports in our country? Would you, for example, like to have a new custom created here — to have somebody from another country go around and spank children with whips dipped in vinegar?"

"You were afraid THAT would happen?"

"Oh, other things, too," he said enigmatically.

I pondered his attitude. Clearly it was a narrow one, allowing of no generosity, no hospitality to visitors from abroad. It was founded in jealousy and selfishness. I told him so.

"Santa Claus, I am sorry to find that you — of all people — have such an attitude. There is no such thing as a truly American Christmas. Almost all of our Christmas customs have come to us from other times and other places. You came from another country to make your place here. The Christmas tree, the ornaments, the mistletoe ritual, the sending of Christmas cards, the act of giving gifts, the burning of the Yule log, the holly decorations, the hanging of the stockings, the symbol of the creche or the manger scene, the act of caroling . . ."

"Oh, people carol in America," he said, "and they sing American songs, like 'Rudolph the Red-Nosed Reindeer' and 'I'm Dreaming of a White Christmas' and lots of other nice American songs."

But such songs as these were not what I had in mind. I

knew that Santa Claus was being argumentative and illogical but I intended to shame him into being more sensible and more helpful to me.

I pointed out that the first hymns written in honor of the Nativity dated to the 5th century, and that the custom of singing carols is credited to St. Francis of Assisi. But of course it goes much further back than the time of the Italian monk who lived from 1182 to 1226.

It seems likely that the joyous impulse of singing grew out of pagan rituals and, after the rites of the heathen winter festivals had become amalgamated with the Christian, caroling took unto itself its own form and fashion. The early Christmas carols were simple because the times were simple. But later the melodies became more sophisticated and the lyrics became polished. One of the earliest of the fine carols was "March of the King." It dates to the 1200's. By the 1400's there were Christmas carols being written in English and, to this period, most scholars ascribe the firm arrival of Christmas carols as we think of them. The church, which had long attempted to suppress dancing and communal singing because they were regarded as paganistic, now became more permissive and man became less willing to accept such disciplines as the prohibition of song.

St. Francis — so it is said — set up a nativity scene in Greccio in the year 1224 as part of the means of telling the Christmas story. The people of Greccio customarily re-enacted nativity plays with real people playing the parts of Mary, Joseph, the shepherds and the Kings. And there must have been song. Earlier Christmas songs must have been mere doggerel. During the time of St. Francis, there came more jubilation and joy in the development of Christmas songs. Some say that St. Francis himself wrote the carol of the celebration for the year 1224. If so, his song has not been handed down to us, though one of the psalms he wrote is known. Part of it, in translation, follows:

> Rejoice to God our helper
> Shout unto God, living and true,
> With the voice of triumph.
> For the Lord in high, terrible;
> A great King over all the earth.
> For the most holy Father of heaven,
> Our King, before ages sent his beloved Son
> from on high, and he was born of the Blessed Virgin
> holy Mary.

But Christmas songs, such as they were, had been sung long before the coming of St. Francis. One by Ambrose, Bishop of Milan and later venerated as a saint, was written in terse Latin phrases:

> Veni, redemptor gentium,
> Ostende partum virginis;
> Miretur omne saeculum;
> Talis decet partus Deum.

This small song which chants in admiration of the goodness in the bringing forth of Jesus in his virginal birth, was written during the life of Ambrose (340?–397) and is one of the earliest of the Christmas songs. However, to the advent of St. Francis we date the coming of the joyousness and exuberance of the Christmas carol.

Santa Claus sat dolorously but, I thought, he seemed to be paying close attention to what I was saying. I had supposed that he, old and experienced as he is, would have known much about the growth of the Christmas carol. But he seemed to be heeding the story.

Martin Luther encouraged congregational singing after the establishment of the Lutheran church in Germany. In the city of Wittenberg the first Protestant hymnal ever published was brought out. The hymnal contained eight songs, including four by Luther himself. It has been said that the merry carols which Luther liked best were those of the people instead of the heavily dogmatic ones of the church. Such songs and the encouragement of congregational singing may have advanced the cause of Protestantism; the people loved to sing songs close to their hearts.

One of Luther's songs was written in 1535 as a Christmas present to one of his sons. The song, "Vom Himmel Hoch" (From Heaven Above), goes like this:

> From Heaven high I come to you
> To bring you tidings good and true

In the second verse, the story begins:

> In Bethlehem of David
> In a manger so small
> Sleeps the Child, the son of Mary
> And Redeemer of all.

The fourth verse:

> Happy hearts now join us in singing,
> Let your lips no silence keep
> For the Lord, the Son of Heaven,
> Saved us from death's dark sleep.

The chorale:

> "Glory to God in highest Heaven
> Who unto us His Son hath given!"
> While angels sing with pious mirth
> A glad new year to all the earth.

Another old favorite, "The First Noel," has a doubtful history also, for no man knows if it came from France or from Germany. But the word, Noel, which now means simply "a Christmas carol," dates back in English history to 1300 (in the form of "Nowell"), when it came into the language from the old French along with related words in Spanish, Portuguese and Italian, all derived from the Latin word "natalem" which itself is derived from the Latin word for birth.

When I asked Santa Claus if he could hum the tune to the song, "Maryland, My Maryland," he smiled and complied, doing so in a rather good, deep and resonant voice which I admired.

Strangely, the tune for that state song is exactly the same as the tune to one of the most popular Christmas songs we have taken from Germany. That old favorite, "O Tannenbaum, O Tannenbaum" (O Christmas Tree, O Christmas tree), bears a melody which is thought to have been used in the middle ages to go with a Latin drinking song.

I wondered if Santa Claus had ever heard the story of the song, "Silent Night," one of the most beautiful to come from Germany — or anywhere. Santa nodded. The story of "Stille Nacht, Heilige Nacht" is surely the best known story of a single song in history. The music was composed by Franz Gruber and the words written by Father Joseph Mohr just to fill a brief need.

In the year 1818 Father Mohr wished to have organ music for the Christmas services in the town of Oberndorf in the Austrian Tyrol. He was disheartened to discover that mice had nibbled a hole in the organ bellows; the organ was not functional. But Father Mohr wished to have a song for the chorus to sing, and he went to his young friend, Franz Gruber. Together they wrote the song which has inspired the world.

The original words:

> Stille Nacht! Heilige Nacht!
> Alles schläft; einsam wacht.
> Nur das traute heilige Paar.
> Holder Knabe im lockigen Haar
> Schläft in himmlischer Ruh.

Stille Nacht! Heilige Nacht!
Gottes Sohn, o wie lacht
Lieb' aus Deinem göttlichen Mund
Da uns schlägt die rettende Stund,
Jesus in Deiner Geburt.

Stille Nacht! Heilige Nacht!
Hirten erst kundgemacht
Durch der Engel Alleluja
Tönt es laut bei fern und nah:
Jesus der Retter ist da!

Somewhat freely translated into English, they are not exactly the words we now sing to the old tune. From the German song of 1818, this is an acceptable translation:

Silent night, holy night
Darkness flies, all is light,
Shepherds hear the Angels sing:
Halleluja, Hail the King,
Jesus the Saviour is here!

Silent Night, Holy night,
Guiding star, lend thy light,
See the Eastern Magi bring,
Gifts and Homage to our King,
Jesus the Savior is here!
Jesus the Savior is here.

Silent night, holiest night,
Wondrous star, lend thy light,
With the angels let us sing,
Hallelujah to the King.
Jesus our Savior is here,
Jesus our Savior is here!

With all due respect to "Rudolph the Red-Nosed Reindeer" and "White Christmas," and the impact they have made upon the American yule season, it is not likely that either of these

two songs — durable as they seem to be — will outlast such songs as those which have lasted these many years.

The first — the absolute first — Christmas carol written in America was done in the Iroquois language of the Huron Indians. It was based on an old French song and given to the Hurons by its author, John de Brebeuf, in 1649.

Christmas has come across oceans and mountains, and it has traveled as a carol, a ceremony, a rite and a belief; by camel and horseback, by canoe, by ship, by every known means of transportation, new and old. The most beautiful and most joyous of the rituals — all grown on their own in many lands — come into the mainstream and have been adopted.

"So, Santa," I said firmly, "when you decline to help the happiest festivities to creep into our country by whatever means, you are harming your own position."

"Well, I know that much of what you are saying is correct," he agreed, "but what is the good in encouraging a gift giver from Belgium to come into my country and perhaps replace me?"

I assured him that it would not happen. "Besides," I said, "as St. Nicholas, you are deeply revered in Belgium. Hundreds of churches are named in your honor there."

"Hundreds of churches, you say? In Belgium? That seems very polite of them," he said, smiling.

"And have you been polite to them?"

"Well, you simply don't realize how quickly a new custom can take hold in the United States. People here are experimental by nature. What is to keep them from instituting a new, or a different, gift giver? Like Klapperbach who lives on Usedom Island at the mouth of the Oder River, maybe."

"Who in the world is Klapperbach?"

"He wears a horse's head and runs around on the island to scare children who don't know their prayers." Santa seemed troubled. "He runs all over that island: Its population is only about 47,000, and he has frightened almost everyone at one time or another. If the children happen to know their prayers, he gives them an apple or a few nuts. But would you want that kind of a Santa Claus here?"

I admitted that I wouldn't. "But, Santa," I said. "You don't have to be afraid of losing your position to a fellow like Klapperbach."

"Maybe not," he said, "but how about Pelzmarte of Swabia? He blackens his face, runs around hitting kids if they don't know their lessons. His name means 'Skin Martin' because he wears skins instead of the pretty red and furlined clothing I wear. Would you like *him*? Or Ashenklas who carries a bag of ashes? Or Knecht Ruprecht who wears garments of skin and straw? Or Bullerklas? Or how would you like a female Santa Claus, like Befana of Italy?"

"Santa," I insisted, "your position here is perfectly safe."

"I think it is if I keep those other people out!"

It took a long time to calm the old fellow but at last he appeared mollified, especially by the praises I heaped upon him. He said, at last, that he was willing to help me invite someone from England. I was not sure that I could trust Santa but he

70

seemed mollified and seemed also to know what he was talking about. People with secret purposes often do. But I decided to trust him one more time. I shouldn't have.

"Who is the correct person in England?" I asked.

"The Boy Bishop," said Santa. "He is the historic gift giver and he is a good person. I suggest you invite him."

I reflected upon Santa's trustworthiness. Could he, I wondered, be purposely leading me into more difficulties? But I reckoned that it would not be so; I could speak English and would be more likely to understand the idioms and the intent in an English sentence instead of those which were translated magically in mid-air. I decided that I would trust the old curmudgeon. I thanked him and returned to my home to prepare for the next session — this one in England.

Later that evening when the wind was cool, I visited the Transvolo Stone and made my wish. I asked for the Boy Bishop. Then I waited. And worried!

9

MEDIEVAL IRREVERENCE

HERE was, indeed, a boy bishop sitting on the Transvolo Stone the next morning and the sight of him made me happy. I was (too soon, alas!) pleased with the advice Santa Claus had given me. I hurried out to greet my young guest.

He rose. "Merry Christmas," he said, in a cultured British accent which made the "merry" sound like "meddy."

"Merry Christmas," I said in my midwestern accent.

He was dressed in the robes of a bishop. He wore a bishop's mitre as a hat and he carried a staff similar to the one which I had felt across my stomach.

The boy bishop was a pleasant looking young man of about 14 years. He was slim and graceful and appeared taller than I would expect a 14 year-old boy to be. Then I realized that it was the tall hat which he wore which made him seem so. He was really much smaller than Americans that age, but then I remembered. People long ago were small.

He looked at me curiously. I knew by his gaze that I was the first American he had ever seen. He was searching for something that was somehow different but I suppose he did not find it except in my size and in my speech. Then, deferentially, he spoke.

"I believe you have summoned me?"

I said that I had. Briefly I explained what I knew about the powers of the Transvolo Stone. He did not appear surprised to learn that we could journey to England so easily. Medieval people were very superstitious; they believed anything.

"I hope I have not inconvenienced you," I said.

"Rather not, I should think," he replied. "You wish to be transported to England with me?"

"Yes."

"I am afraid that will not be possible."

Well, I thought, here we go again. Now what? I waited for an explanation but the boy bishop simply stood there, his head bowed as much as his tall, heavy hat would permit. After a polite interval I turned on what has been called American brashness. I was direct.

"Well, why won't it be possible?" I asked with a testy note in my voice. Nothing seemed to be going right for me on my planned visits to the Christmas places in the world.

The young man reached a hand into his voluminous robes and drew out a rolled piece of yellow parchment.

"I have here a document which prevents me from escorting you into and round about England." (Englishmen say "round" where we say "around.") He unrolled the document and held it toward me. I moved to his side and looked at the parchment over his shoulder. I could see that it was an ancient proclamation signed by King Henry VIII. It was dated July 22, 1541. I glanced over the first few lines, then read a proclamation against boy bishops and lords of misrule.

King Henry had commanded that "from henceforth all such superstitions be lost and clyerlye extinguisshed throughowte all this his realms and dominions, forasmoche as the same doo resemble their rather the unlawfull superstition of gentilitie, than the pure and sincere religion of Christe." It was signed with the cramped, tortured autograph of the bluff King Hal.

73

"I don't understand it," I told the boy bishop as I sat down on the Transvolo Stone. "The language is strange."

"It's a strong proclamation which says that all such superstitions as, for example, that of the boy bishop be done away with."

"King Henry wasn't a very good speller," I said. "What is this phrase, 'clyerlye extinguisshed.' It's old English, I know, but what does it mean?"

"Cleverly extinguished," said the boy.

"But I don't see anything in the proclamation which tells his reason for wanting to have you 'cleverly extinguished.'"

"Yes, he gives his reason. Look at this phrase: 'extinguisshed throughowte all this his realms and dominions, forasmoche as the same do resemble their rather the unlawfull superstition of gentilitie, than the pure religion of Christe.'"

"What does he mean — gentilitie?"

"Oh, that is an old use of the word. It means paganism."

"I don't understand how a bishop can represent anything

74

paganistic," I said. "Rather, it seems to me that a bishop more surely represents church than paganism."

The boy sighed.

"It is a long story. You remember this was the time of the beginning of the Reformation, the massive 16th-century religious revolution against the Roman Catholic Church. It resulted in the establishment of Protestant churches. And perhaps you remember the troubles between King Henry and the Pope."

I did, a little.

Henry, a strong king in a compact nation with a powerful central government, had vied with the pope over ecclesiastical jurisdiction. The political break, with the pope on one side and Henry and parliament on the other, came when Henry wanted to divorce his Catholic wife, Catherine of Aragon. Henry declared the marriage invalid under ecclesiastical law because Catherine was the widow of his brother. The pope, however, ruled that the marriage was a legal one. Henry took his way, as he often did. He simply married Anne Boleyn (in 1533) and two months later demanded that the Archbishop of Canterbury must pronounce his divorce from Catherine.

One result of this high handed liberty was that the pope promptly excommunicated Henry. The following year Henry took his revenge against the pope. He had the parliament pass an act appointing him, and each of his successors, the "supreme head of the Church of England," an act which established an independent national Anglican church. It is the reason that England as a nation is not of the Roman Catholic faith.

I mused over this for a time but my thought soon turned to Christmas and the boy bishop.

"You would obey this proclamation by a king who wrote it in anger more than 400 years ago?" I asked him.

"People of England are law abiding people."

75

"Perhaps so. But I would not obey such a proclamation. Besides, I hoped to go to England today — with you."

"I am sorry."

"Even so. But is there an opportunity for me to go there with somebody else? Santa Claus for example?"

"We have no Santa Claus in England. We call him Father Christmas. He is rather taller and rather more slender than your gift giver, but otherwise he is similar."

"Would he escort me to England?"

"I fear that he would not. He guards his domains as jealously as did King Henry. I suspect that he would not like to be invited as a second thought. He regards himself as Number One and he does not approve of me or of the people who associate themselves with me."

"Have you had a run-in with him?"

"I do not understand the term run-in."

I reflected that England does not care for our casualness in phraseology and in our slang.

"Run-in — you know, a rhubarb, an altercation, a quarrel."

"No. He has not quarreled with me. Rather, he pretends that I do not exist."

"You do, don't you? You are real?"

"To some persons. It may be possible that the festival of the boy bishop will return some day. When it does I shall be ready."

"In effect, then, you are what they used to call a pretender to the throne."

"Not to the throne but to the domain of Father Christmas. I would like to be the gift giver, I confess."

I rolled my eyes in mock awe. Comes the revolution, I thought. But I did not say it. I had stopped being surprised at contention among the Christmas figures of the world. Here was a contender out of medieval times. Does ambition never cease?

"If you cannot take me there," I said, "I wonder if you would tell me about Christmas in England."

"Gladly. But, sir, the Christmas festivals I know are those of long ago. You must realize that I have not been part of the Christmas functions of England for many years."

"How many years? Christmas customs, I believe, tend to be traditional and people cling to them. I happen to know that the English are lovers of tradition."

"We are. But I cannot say which customs have been dropped and which customs have been added. I have not attended an English Christmas for . . . oh, a very long time."

"Since Henry's proclamation in 1541?"

"Well, no," he said slowly. "I was outlawed by the proclamation in that year, of course, but during the reign of Queen Mary I was allowed some few more Christmases. Father Christmas was very angry about it but he, of course, could do nothing. Royalty reigns supreme, even over traditions."

He explained further. Queen Mary I (1516–1558) was, of course, the daughter of Henry VIII by his first wife, Catherine of Aragon, who chose to be of the Catholic faith like her mother. When Mary was crowned in July, 1553, she restored the privilege of Mass and aided in re-establishing the authority of the pope in England. Futhermore, she wiped out some of the bans and religious innovations made by her father. Therefore, during the reign of Mary Tudor, the boy bishop, apparently, had been the important Christmas figure.

"But you are under a ban again?" I asked. "How did that come to be?"

"After the death of Mary, Elizabeth became the queen. Unlike her half sister Mary, she was Protestant. Elizabeth was the daughter of Henry VIII and his second wife, Anne Boleyn, who was Protestant. And Queen Elizabeth thought that the festival of the boy bishop was 'popish' so she rejected it. That's when Father Christmas came back into authority."

"Hence, I suppose, you have not been active in any Christmas in modern times? Not for — let's see — 410 years?"

"That is quite correct," said the boy.

"But that is such a long, long time! Christmas has changed greatly since then. Are you sure that England was observing Christmas 400 years ago?"

"Sir, Christmas came to England long before it came to the United States," said the boy with a little more anger in his voice than seemed necessary. "Christmas was brought to England by St. Augustine of Canterbury in the year 604! That's one thousand three hundred and sixty-five years ago!"

It seemed persuasive enough for me. I encouraged the boy bishop to discuss Christmas during the period of his administration.

The boy bishop, he explained, is really a legendary version of the original St. Nicholas, also a bishop and a young one. That bishop was associated with children, was helpful to them and good to them and, hence, became the patron saint of Christmas.

"By the way," I said as casually as I could, "how old are you, bishop?" I meant, of course, his legendary age, not the real age of St. Nicholas who became the Bishop of Myra in the 4th century. Under the circumstances, I thought the question was permissible.

"I have been told that Americans tend to ask impertinent questions," the boy answered.

It meant that he did not intend to answer my question. I thought it would be just as well. It was strange to recall that I was sitting on a stone chatting with a boy who was fifteen hundred years old!

I asked him about the traditional boar's head of England. I had seen so many pictures of English holiday scenes and the boar's head, complete with apple in the mouth.

It goes back a long time, the boy told me, back to a day when a student at Queen's College, Oxford, was walking through Shotover Forest and was deeply involved in reading Aristotle as he wandered. Then, without warning, a wild boar charged at him so swiftly and fiercely that the student had no time to draw his sword. The scholar quickly jammed his book into the animal's open jaws and down his throat. The boar choked to death.

The scholar, wanting his book back, cut off the boar's head, retrieved his Aristotle and brought both trophies — the book and the boar's head — back to his fellow scholars.

The scholars at Oxford may have been in a playful mood. They roasted the head and carried it into the great dining hall with much levity and ceremony. It commenced the tradition in England in general and in Queen's College in particular.

The tradition grew and was adopted by England's lords and ladies of medieval times. Then, with the advent of Oliver Cromwell, the tradition and custom were outlawed, quite naturally. Cromwell, in fact, banned Christmas in 1647.

A few days before Christmas of that year, Cromwell ordered town criers to walk through the streets calling out that there was a new law which banned Christmas festivities. The English, great lovers of freedom, were angry enough to riot, which they did. But Cromwell and his Puritans managed to keep Christmas illegal until his death in 1658. Despite him, many Englishmen secretly celebrated the festival.

When King Charles II came to the throne and brought Christmas back, folk singers of the period popularized a ballad which was commonly sung in the public houses of England:

> Now thanks to God for Charles' return
> Whose absence made old Christmas mourn,
> For then we scarcely did it know
> Whether it Christmas were, or no.

Although the custom of the boar's head festival returned, it never again reached its previous popularity with the people.

But the ritual of preparation, the boy bishop went on, was almost as important as the serving of the garish meal.

The head was boned, he said, except that the jawbones and tusks were left in to help the head keep its natural shape. Then stuffing was prepared from sausage meat, pieces of ox tongue, truffles, apples, mushrooms, nuts and spices.

This stuffing was tucked inside the boar's head with a mixture of minced pig's liver, onions, chopped apples, sage and rosemary. Some of the stuffing was moistened with Calvados wine.

The boar's head was then wrapped in cloth and boiled a full eight hours, with hot water added as it was needed. The ears of the boar, which had been cut off earlier and boiled separately, were then replaced with little skewers. It was served thus, with apple in mouth.

Wild boars, of course, became scarce in England, though in the days of the Druids they were common. As the boar disappeared the pig took over in the ceremony of the boar's head.

The boy bishop stopped to ponder. Then he asked: "Does England, still observe the boar's head ceremonies? Or has America adopted it? I have been out of circulation there for many years," he added sadly.

I thought it unlikely and said so.

He remembered from his "youth," he said, that animals played an important part in the Christmas festival. He recollected a sign which he had seen often in his day, and he described it.

The sign showed a rooster crowing in Latin, "Christus natus est!" (Christ is born!). A raven responds by asking "Quando?" (When?). A crow answers him with the words, "Hac nocte." (This night). An ox lows, "Ubi?" (Where?). A lamb bleats the final answer: "Bethlehem!"

A very old sign, the boy bishop averred, and one he remembered to be common during his reign.

Christmas festivities had been both popular and unpopular at various times, the boy told me. He remembered a sermon he had heard from a noted theologian who commented, "If all the devils in hell had put their heads together to devise a feast that should utterly scandalize Christianity, they could not have improved on this one."

Some of the customs were wild, the boy said. During one period, an entire 12 days — beginning on Christmas eve — was a time of wild jollity. It was not only the custom — it was the law — that a person called The Lord of Misrule reigned in the palace of the king and in the palace of every nobleman "of honor and good worship (though he may be) spiritual or temporal."

A contemporary, Philip Stubbes, a stern Puritan, wrote that "My Lorde of Misrule, crowned with great solemnity and adopteth as king . . . chuseth twenty, forty, three-score or one hundred lusty guttes (fellows) like himself to wait upon his majesty and guard his noble person . . . Bells in the number of 20 or 40 were tied about either leg of the lord's men," which he described as a "heathen company."

They wore masks, said Stubbes, and rode contrived man-made dragons and hobby horses, and they marched and "rode" toward church with "pipers piping, drummers thundering, bellys iynling" (an excellent verb! some bells do!).

The lord and his parties were "shameless" in church, even though the preacher might be preaching or praying. They "carry on like Devils incarnate," he wrote, "with such a confused noise that a mane cannot hear his owne voice." And the foolish people in the congregation, "they looke, they stare, they laugh, they fleere (grimace) and mount upon . . . pewes to see."

The misrulers, after church, danced all day and perhaps all night, and onlookers brought food and money to these "hell-houndes," wrote Stubbe. "Hethenrie, devilrie, drunkenness, unrestrainted luste, pride and what not" marked the party.

These Lords of Misrule were given considerable power, the boy bishop said (with a fleere!). There is still extant a document dated 1634, prepared by Richard Evelyn, Esquire, who was high sheriff of Surrey and Sussex shires (counties). It appointed one Owen Flood, a trumpeter, to be Lord of Misrule. As the Lord, he was empowered and given "free leave to command all and every person whatsoever, as well as servants and others, to be at his command whensoever he shall sound his Trumpett or Musick, and to do him good service as though I were present myselfe, at their perils (if they do not).

"I give full power and authority to his Lordship to breake all lockes, bolts, barres, doores, and latches, and to fling up all

82

doores out of hendges to come at those who presume to disobey his Lordship's commands."

Such a function, said the boy bishop, was clearly a piece of reactionary business relating to the days of pagans and their irreverent rituals.

He lapsed into silence. I thought he was contemplating something which he did not wish to tell me. I gave his thoughts food.

"The Lord of Misrule has died away," I said. "I am quite sure there are no such rites these days. But can you think of other things that were odd?"

He nodded. "Do you practice the Feast of the Fools in America? Or does Europe still have such ceremonies?"

I had not ever heard of it and said so. Then, seeming to speak a little more swiftly than before — as though to rush through embarrassment — he explained.

"These feasts, I suppose, were a recoil from the dogmatic rituals of Christianity and the ponderous church services of the times. Low ranking clerks and members of the clergy of the 1400's or so held these festivals around Christmastime. They would do odd things within the walls of the church. They entered the church dressed in all manner of odd ways — like women, or panders or minstrels and they would sing wanton, lewd songs. Then, in front of the altar, they would gabble merrily and eat black porridge even while others were saying Mass."

"How odd and irreverent," I observed.

"Yes. They would play at dice there, and run and leap through the church, climbing on the pews and making silly remarks and when they had tired of it they would have themselves driven about town in an open cart while they would act like imbeciles and cause the people to laugh at their antics."

"Odd. Very odd," I said.

"You do not do this any more?" he asked.

"Nope. Not ever."

"Not in France? Nor England?"

"Surely not!" I said firmly. "Was this Feast of the Fools led by the King of Misrule also?"

"No."

"By whom then?"

He looked embarrassed but he answered.

"By the boy bishop."

He explained that he believed it to be a result of the vulgarity of the lower classes of the period and the grim rules of the church. But he would tell me no more about the fools' festival.

Boy bishops, he said, were elected from among the choir boys. It was in their power during their reign in office to command church dignitaries to obey mischievous demands.

Boy bishops, sometimes called Nicholas Bishop, according to my visitor, were elected in almost every church or parish of medieval England in the Middle Ages. It was such forms of irreverent merriment which caused King Henry VIII to issue his proclamation, but he also had other purposes when he did so.

My guest appeared tired, but he asked if any country still observed what he called "Boxing Day." I had heard that it is observed in England still, but I think nowhere else. I was unaware of the details of it. I asked what they were.

"December 26th is, as you know, St. Stephen's Day," he said, "though all of England called it (and still does, I suppose) Boxing Day. It is nearly as important as Christmas because, by ancient custom, the village pastor or priest (when England was Catholic) would open the poor box at the church and distribute all of the contents to people who needed money or help.

"Later," said the boy, "it came to be a custom to give gifts of presents or money to poor people or to servants."

I touched the boy's arm to stop him.

"But why did they call it Boxing Day?"

"For the simple reason that the gifts were customarily placed in boxes," he said tersely.

"But," I protested, "today not very many people in England can afford servants, so isn't the custom about ready to die?"

"I think not. I suppose that today, as in my day, the gifts were given to public servants or any person who performed some service of work or assistance for you professionally."

I recalled having heard that postmen and policemen and chimney sweeps and milkmen, newsboys, cabdrivers and street cleaners — these people and those who performed similar services — are given gifts on Boxing Day.

The boy bishop appeared tired. It was, I knew, from sitting on the Transvolo Stone the long day. It was not a comfortable seat. The boy lapsed into silence.

"I am sorry that I have not been able to visit your wonderful country," I told him, "but I appreciate your visit and your explanation of how things were."

"You are very welcome, sir," he said, rising. "Please come and visit when you can. You would like my people and my country."

"But when could I come?" I asked him seriously.

"Sometime when I am in power," he said. Then he was gone. I realized that he still aspired to his strange throne, and that he may have been still eager for the overthrow of Father Christmas.

10

GRANDMOTHER BABUSHKA
AND RUSSIA

I HAD a twinge of apprehension the next day when I gave the Transvolo Stone three choices. I would like, I said in the proper place during the usual incantation, to go to Denmark or Finland — or to Russia. I had decided that if any invited guests were going to have their feelings hurt, it would be the Transvolo Stone, not I, who hurt them. I returned to the house to wait.

The next time I looked out of the window, scarcely an hour after placing my formal request, I saw that I had a visitor. But this one was a surprise to me. It was an old lady, and I was unable to guess her nationality. She was very old, very wrinkled, very haggish in appearance. I strolled outside and spoke politely.

"Good day!"

She said nothing, but she handed me a package which I opened at once. She had made me a present of a pair of red boots, boy-size.

"Thank you, grandmother," I said. "Could you tell me where you have come from and your name?"

"You have addressed me correctly. My name is Babushka which, in Russian, means grandmother."

"Are you the gift giver for the children of the Soviet Union? Are you the Russian version of the American Santa Claus?"

She was silent for a moment.

"I *was*," she said at last. She said it dolefully.

"You were? Does this mean that you are not now?"

"Somewhat. But my place in the legend is slowly being taken over by Deydushka Moroz. You would call him Grandfather Frost. But that isn't what I would call him." She said that last with bitterness.

"Do you have another name for him?"

"Yes. Several. But I would not use those names in company."

"You are angry with Grandfather Frost?"

"No. But throughout all of Russia's great history, I have been the gift giver, even though not a jolly one. Deyd Moroz has been taking more and more of my territory until some day I shall have none left. The job of giving gifts is historically mine. I earned it at the time that the wise men were searching for the Infant Jesus."

She explained the legend: When the Magi were journeying to Bethlehem to visit the manger where the Child Jesus lay, they lost their way. When they stopped to ask an old woman for the direction, she deliberately misdirected them.

For her evil deed, she was condemned to walk the earth forever to give presents to the little children of the world. This was the penance she must pay. Customarily her gifts are golden slippers to little girls and red boots to little boys.

"But," I asked, "are you not the helper of Grandfather Frost? Many countries have both a gift giver and a helper. I would think this would be true in Russia as well."

"Humph!" said the old grandmother. "He has a helper in Russia all right, but it is not I. Naturally not! I am not *pretty* enough. No, the Grandfather Frost has a helper — a pretty girl named Segurocha, or Snow Maiden. I have been here for centuries doing my work. But I am not allowed these days to help give the gifts."

"I am truly sorry to learn that you are unhappy," I said. "But I hope that I may ask you to take me to your country to observe the celebration of Christmas."

"Christmas? What is that?" she asked, her brows pulled into an unattractive, wrinkled frown. She paused and, before I could answer her, her face lightened and she said, "Oh, *Kolyada*!" Kolyada is the Russian word for Christmas.

"Why do you choose the Soviet Union to visit for such an occasion?" she asked with seriousness. "Don't you realize that we do not have a Christmas holiday? Since Communists came into power in Russia in 1917, Christmas has not been officially observed there. Besides, December 25 is a regular working day in the Soviet Union. Christmas has no religious connotations at all. When it comes the time of the gift giving, it is not to celebrate the birth of the Christ Child. It is to celebrate the New Year. We observe it on January 6."

"Is it possible that nobody there celebrates the birth of Christ?"

"Yes, some do. But they do it unobtrusively, quietly, in their churches and in their homes."

"Could you take me to such a place?" I asked contritely.

She nodded her head. Then I heard the familiar "whoosh!" like the sound of a tornado or a speeding train.

I found myself standing with Grandma Babushka on Petrovka Street in Moscow in front of the huge Mostborg Department Store. In the front window was a thin, white-bearded man who at first I took to be Santa Claus. A second, closer look, however, was sufficient for me to determine that he was not. The difference was in his thin body and his long, heavy robe patterned after those which the old Russian nobility used to wear.

The collar of his jacket was somewhat military in design but he had black boots like those worn by Santa Claus. His hair was long and white, and his beard was full enough to hide most of his face. His cheeks were red and he was laughing in a big, booming voice.

"You have Christmas trees here," I said to Babushka as I indicated a well decorated tree which stood in the window near Grandfather Frost.

"We do not call it a Christmas tree," she said. "We call it a yolka, for the new year. It means a New Year tree."

The yolka was very like our Christmas tree though it was decorated somewhat differently. Besides twinkling with gay little lights, the tree was trimmed with tangerines, gilded nuts and some modern plastic ornaments similar to those used in the United States.

Grandma and I walked the streets of downtown Moscow. I noted strange looking people in the crowd of many faces, strange to my Midwestern American eyes. It was not strange, however, that Russian faces showed such wide diversity. Long ago, with the Grand Duchy of Moscow as a nucleus, the Russian state had expanded in every direction since the 15th century. By the turn of the 18th century, Russia was by far the largest state in Europe, reaching from the Baltic Sea and the Arctic Ocean and the Caspian Sea in the South; from the borderlines of Austria and Prussia in the West to the Pacific in the East. Later additions, including portions of Poland and Finland, so increased the size of Russia that it covered more than eight million square miles. (The continental United States comprises only slightly more than three million square miles by comparison.)

Such a vast territory is inhabited by many tribes of peoples who differ greatly in customs and languages. There are more than 60 quite distinct ethnic groups there, including Latvians, Slovaks, Lithuanians, Germans, Estonians, Finns, Serbs, Lapps, Rumanians, Jews, Poles, Czechs, Hungarians, Kalmucks, Tar-

tars, Armenians and Scandinavians. The so-called White Russians and Little Russians (Ukrainians) form about two thirds of the population.

So it was that, as we strolled down Petrovka Street, I was to observe faces which appeared to range from southern Slavic to Asiatic-Oriental, the latter people descended, perhaps, from the Mongol hordes of Khan and other Asian war lords who charged over this land.

We strolled through Moscow's Hall of Columns where the city's largest yolka stands in the main hall. A Mongolian attendant told us that in the next few days almost 100,000 Russian children would attend special holiday (not Christmas) performances of theatrical artists, clowns and other entertainers. The holiday season begins in Moscow on December 30 and comes to a finale on January 10.

Moscow's best and most famous Grandfather Frost would be there, of course, the guard told us. I could not resist asking the question which came to mind.

"Is Grandma Babushka going to be here, too, to help him?"

The guard looked startled for a moment, then he laughed.

"Haven't you heard, comrade? Grandfather Frost has a new girl friend!"

Grandma Babushka said nothing whatsoever. I had noted, of course, that she was invisible to the stalwart guard who stood grinning at me.

I turned to study what reaction Grandma Babushka would have to the guard's joke. I was surprised to see her slowly disintegrate into air. One moment she was there fully; the next moment she was a fading shadow, and the next, she was quite gone. It startled me so much that I turned to the guard to see if he had noticed anything. He had not. He stood there, his legs spread wide and a great smile on his face. Then it happened.

I heard a loud noise, "smack!" and I saw the guard tumble
backward, almost falling. The smile was gone from his face
and a look of amazement was there in its place. He put his
hand to his cheek and jabbered something at me. Then he
moved forward, grabbing at me with both hands. I could see
that his left cheek had turned bright red and I knew then that
Grandma Babushka had given him a hearty slap.

"I didn't do it," I told the guard. "Let me go."

But he held onto me tightly. He had not seen the blow, of

course, and he had been looking directly at me when it came. I could see that he was perplexed; I was the only one close enough to smite him and yet he knew that I had not done so. I struggled a little and finally he let me go.

But the look on his face was one of such awe and terror that I could not help grinning at him.

"What happened?" I asked.

"I don't know," he said, no longer mistrusting me. "I suddenly got this terrible pain in my face. I thought you had struck me."

"No, no. I didn't touch you."

"Yes. Well, it seems I am about to have a terrible toothache," he said, his voice carrying a tone of wonderment.

I couldn't stop grinning.

"Does it amuse you to see a man in pain with a toothache?" he asked petulantly.

I tried to stop grinning. I turned to move away and in that instant I heard the same sound again, this time sharper, louder. "Smack!"

When I looked around, the guard was sitting on the floor of the Hall of Columns, his eyes watering and a look of absolute disbelief on his face. Grandma Babushka was getting in a few licks! And, against my will, I grinned at him again. Then I retreated.

"You, Comrade, are nothing but a first class *schinderhannes!*" he shouted at my back.

But I moved away. I was tempted to tell him that I thought there were no classes, like first class anything, or second or third, in the Soviet Union. But I resisted the temptation and held my tongue. I wondered about the word he had used. What did it mean? I learned later that schinderhannes is a German word meaning "Cruel Jack," a term once applied to people who make their living by hauling away dead horses and skinning them for their hides. I do not know how such a word got into the language of a Russian, but I think it an excellent word.

Alone, I moved down the streets of Moscow. I hoped I had not lost my guide. But I had. Grandmother Babushka was gone.

I wandered through the big railway station, noting that most of the men moving about wore the Astrakhan hats which are now popular among men in the United States. They are warm and comfortable, a protection from the fierce cold of the country. They were named for the city of the same name which sits on the banks of the Volga River, but "astrakhan" is really sheep's wool.

I had discovered during my visits to foreign countries that I could read (magically, I suppose) the signs in any language and understand them, too.

I was amused to note that the railroad station bore signs announcing various "categories" (not "classes") of passengers. I was to learn that "first category passengers" may ride two or four people to a compartment with berths. "Second category" passengers ride in compartments with nine uncushioned wooden bunks hung three deep on the wall. "Third category passengers" travel in similar compartments but the bunks cannot be reserved. There are also luxury cars for very important people of the politbureau.

So I assumed that when a Soviet citizen says that there are no "classes" in his country he really means it. But he doesn't mean that there is absolute equality there. What he means is that private individuals are not permitted to control land, resources or other elements of production which could enable them to exploit other people who do not own such resources. But I found it difficult to understand that in a society which protests that it has no classes of people, there are "categories" of them, as shown by the signs in the railroad station. I found it difficult to differentiate between a "class" and a "category."

It was apparent to me that Grandma Babushka had abdicated from her duties as a guide and that I was now in a foreign country without a visa and, indeed, without a right to be there. I guessed that it would be difficult for Russian immigration authorities to believe my story about the powers of the Transvolo Stone. I decided to go cautiously, to learn what I could and to get home by whatever means came to me. But obviously, I would need to find someone to talk with.

I found a friend in Yakov Aleksandrovich Tyutchev. Yakov, is the Russian version of Jacob.

I met Yakov in Moscow's Central Park of Rest and Culture. With his small daughter, Galya, he was standing in the children's village which had been converted for the holiday occasion into a fairyland of ice sculptures. Carved out of huge blocks of ice were some traditional Russian figures of fairyland or legend — Grandfather Frost stood next to the great legendary Russian giant, Bogatyr; and near them was the icy figure of the huge gray wolf that helped Czarevitch Ivan to get the firebird. All very beautiful.

It was not difficult to become friends with Yakov. He recognized me by my clothing and manner as an American. And, just as we are curious about citizens of the Soviet Union, so are they curious about us. Besides, Yakov had learned some English which he spoke with a profound accent and he would be happy to have a chance to use his English and improve it. In foreign countries, as in the United States, everybody who has a command of an alien tongue always welcomes the opportunity to practice. Thus we became friends.

With Yakov and Galya as my guides, we strolled through department stores that looked very like our own shops during the Christmas season.

One could buy strings of painted cardboard animals, dolls, toy trucks, wagons, bicycles, games, toy automobiles, and wind-up Russian bears all dressed up in maroon colored velvet and playing a toy balalaika. Galya was pleased with a charming little doll house made of branches and looking like one of the traditional log cabins of northern rural Russia. When I bought it for her (for $2.50) in Russian coin loaned to me by Yakov, I won a friend for life.

I was interested in observing that the Soviet Union has apparently lost the armaments race with the United States — in the toy stores. I saw an occasional pop gun or pistol but nothing more to display military might. Soviet toy manufacturers seem to avoid the military things which are so common in the American toy shops. I saw no tanks, hand grenades, imitation steel helmets, jet bombers or machine guns.

Although the Soviet Union is atheistic and generally communistic, it appears that Grandfather Frost knows no politics, no religion. He is accepted by the children as a benign fellow who brings presents at New Year's, hauling them to each child's home by means of reindeer. I did, however, see an advertisement in one of the stores which showed Grandfather Frost and his sleigh being transported through the hemisphere by means of Russian sputniks!

Christmas is not a Soviet holiday. The stores and the offices and the shops are open just as on ordinary days because, in the Soviet Union, there is no such thing as Christmas, no such holy being as the Christ Child.

But, of course, the Soviet Union and its satellite countries have not been able to stamp out Christmas. The church bells ring on that day just as they have always done. Each year during the season, there is a huge children's party in the gaily decorated St. George's Hall of the Kremlin.

The Russian Orthodox Church which has an estimated 35 million members, Yakov told me, tries consciously to keep the Christmas period a religious one. The church usually offers

Mass not on December 25, but on January 6. The reason for this is because the Soviet Union operates generally on a calendar which is 13 days behind ours.

Yakov tried to explain things to me with great patience and much tact so as not to seem to offend me. I asked him quite plainly what Christmas means to the average citizen of the Soviet Union. He hesitated, searching for an answer. Finally he said we must wait until we visited his house. He would show me then.

On the way to Yakov's home, we passed St. Basil's Cathedral, a 16th century building with the characteristic onion shaped domes which testify to the Byzantine influence in Russian architecture of an earlier period. But after the revolution there has been little architectural achievement, and even after the reconstruction period the only buildings of note were industrial establishments made of reinforced concrete.

Yakov and Galya and I chatted amiably as we traveled. I was surprised to see several shops called *Amerikankas,* a word which translates generally to "American Woman."

Yakov explained this, and it emerged as a rather good compliment. The stores are dry cleaning establishments and the word is applied to them because it evokes an image of cleanliness, fashion, and promptness. A rather complimentary picture of the American female, I thought. It stirred some pride in me, too.

Yakov lived 20 miles out in the country in a small cottage with his wife, Maria, a robust, jolly woman of great hospitality. She addressed her husband merrily, calling him "Kalita." When I asked him the reason for this term of affection, he looked embarrassed and translated it for me: "Moneybag!" Yakov, apparently, was the keeper of the household purse.

The family lived in a good house for the region, one which had been partially smashed by a German bomb during the re-

96

treat of World War II. Yakov, himself home from the wars, had rebuilt it with Maria working at his side like a manual laborer. But his house now had two rooms, each about 10 feet square. A small porch had been erected next to the back door and in winter it served as a woodshed. A little Christmas tree stood as far from the square iron stove as they could get it. I observed that electric lights were not yet in use in Yakov's district. His tree had candles on the branches.

"You will stay with us overnight?" Maria asked.

I saw no place where a guest could sleep so I declined, but Yakov sensed my reason and smiled. "When we have a guest, we make up a bed right on top of the stove," he said. "It is very comfortable."

Very warm, too, I would imagine. But I knew I must not stay too long. I reminded Yakov that he was to show me what "Christmas" is in the Soviet Union. He took down a Russian dictionary, searched through the pages and then pointed out the paragraph to me.

It read: "Christmas. The birthday of the mythical founder of Christianity." Clear enough.

Maria and her daughter prepared a traditional Christmas dinner — goose stuffed with apples. Yakov, however, insisted upon having sips of vodka after almost every bit of food, with several different kinds of wine in between. He became very jolly and talkative.

When several of Galya's friends came to visit her, the room was crowded and gay. They decided they would teach me a Christmas game.

Galya went to the shed and came back with several handfuls of grain. She placed little piles of grain on the kitchen floor while her friends gathered symbols for each pile. Galya went into the yard and soon returned with a hen which gave the impression that it would rather be asleep.

Next to each of the piles of grain, the girls placed one of the symbols they had gathered — a coin, a needle, a finger ring, a bit of coal, a bit of green twig from the yolka. They then set the hen loose to choose her own pile of grain.

The game — surely so ancient that it pre-dated general literacy among Russians of yore — was this: If the hen went first to the grain pile next to the coin, it was taken to mean that riches would come to the girl who had taken this turn to set the hen free. If the hen chose the pile near the needle, it would mean, I was told, that the girl would have to work hard and sew all the rest of her life. If the pile near the ring was the first selected, it meant an early marriage. If the hen chose that near the charcoal, it foretold death in the family. If the pile near the green twig was chosen, it meant good crops for the coming year.

Each girl took her own turn with the hen. At Galya's turn, the tired hen elected to peck at the pile near the ring. She blushed.

It was getting late now, and I took my leave. I explained to my new friends that I had my own means of transportation, and I did.

I walked into the front yard and said my special words to bring me back to my Transvolo Stone.

Something, though, went wrong with directions. After the sound of the great "whoosh" came to my ears, I looked around and found myself somewhere in Wales. I knew it because I saw a sign bearing the following place-name:

Llanfairpwllgwynggyllgogerychwyrbrrrobwlltysiliogogogoch.

Only the little country of Wales (136 miles long) would have such a long name for such a little town.

I was leaning against the side of a bus station, I who am not ordinarily a leaning type of a fellow. A small, smiling man approached me.

11

CHRISTMAS IN WALES

"NADOLIG LAWEN!" said the small Welshman.
I was surprised to hear him say Merry Christmas (*really* Christmas Merry) in the language of the land because it is a language which is slowly slipping away from the populace. And such a beautiful, difficult language it is!

"Merry Christmas!" I responded. I moved away from the wall of the station because I knew my leaning position would make me appear to be indolent. Indolence is not looked upon favorably in Wales. Then I added, "I am surprised and pleased to hear a Welshman use his own tongue."

My words pleased him. The official language of Wales is English because Wales is a principality of the United Kingdom of Great Britain. Hence English is spoken by virtually every person in Wales. Only a very few speak Welsh only, and about 30 percent of the population speaks both English and Welsh.

"We do use common Welsh expressions," said the small man, "and we hold to portions of our language by this means. The term for Merry Christmas is very commonly used here, even by people who speak no Welsh at all."

He paused, then smiled.

"I'm guessing that you're an American tourist. You looked forlorn and lost and I wondered if I could do anything to help you. My name is Parri. Gwynfa Parri."

I introduced myself and we shook hands.

"I seem to be lost," I told him. "What city is this?"

"Llandudno. You're in Caernarvonshire in North Wales on the coastline of the Irish Sea. A resort town."

"A very pretty one," I said, and I meant it. I could see two tall rocky bluffs high on the side of the city. Their tops were covered with the yellow blossoms of gorse, even though it was (I supposed) December. The mountainous hills are named Orme — the Great Orme and the Little Orme.

"Thank you," Mr. Parri said. "Are you here on a visit?"

"Frankly, I was in hopes of seeing Santa Claus. What Welsh name do you use to designate him?" I asked.

"Strangely enough, there is no Welsh name for Santa Claus. We simply speak of our version of Santa Claus as Father Christmas, the same as the one in England."

"Could you tell me where I could find him? I'm rather in need of a guide. My purpose in being here is to try to learn what I can of the Welsh Christmas."

"Look you," he said. "Father Christmas would be busy at this time. But I would be pleased to tell you what you would like to know. I have many relatives in the United States, quite a few of them named Morgan. Would you know any of them?" he asked. Then he smiled. "I keep forgetting how huge the United States is. You couldn't possibly know any of the Morgan clan."

"Yes, I do. Morgan is a very common name in my country. I know at least three families which can boast the name of Morgan."

Again I had pleased this proud Welshman. It is often found that the people of small nations understand and love their lands more enthusiastically than those who live in great countries. To know it, one must suppose, is to love it.

Mr. Parri asked about other typical Welsh names common in

the United States. Did I ever happen to hear of any family names Jones, or Lloyd, or Williams, or Evans, or Powell, or Howell?

I assured him that these were some of the most familiar names in the United States.

"Owen?" he asked. "Or Richards? Griffith?"

I grinned at him and told him that of course I had met people with such purely Welsh names. Mr. Parri looked so happy that I thought he was going to burst out in song — in the Welsh national anthem, of course, "Hen wlad fy Nhaden." But he did not. Instead he sang the Welsh words to the familiar carol, "Stand Up, Stand Up for Jesus."

That familiar and beautiful song is here rendered in the Welsh language and the English; thanks to Gwynfa:

Cyfodwch dros yr Iesu!	Stand up, stand up for Jesus!
Yn wrol fyddin gref;	Ye soldiers of the cross,
Ei faner wen freninol	Lift high His royal banner,
Dyrchefwch hyd y nef;	It must not suffer loss;
Mae'n arwain Ei fyddinoedd	From victory unto victory,
I drechu uffern fawr;	His army shall He lead,
Teyrnasu raid i'n Iesu	Till every foe is vanquished
Yn Frenin nef a llawr.	And Christ is Lord indeed.
Cyfodwch dros yr Iesu!	Stand up, stand up for Jesus!
Ni raid ymdrechu'n hir;	The trumpet call obey;
Os twrf y rhyfel heddyw,	Forth to His mighty conflict,
Y fory canu clir;	In this His glorious day;
Yr hwn sydd yn gorchfygu	Ye that are men now serve Him,
Gaiff goron ddydd a ddaw,	Each 'gainst unnumbered foes,
A bythol gyd-deyrnasu	Let courage rise with danger,
A'r Iesu'r ochr draw.	And strength to strength oppose.

He was interested in first names. He asked me if I had ever met anybody named as he was — Gwynfa. I assured him that I had not.

"Ah, well," he said without surprise. "My father, a minister,

gave me the name because it means Paradise and I confess I have not met anybody in Wales, either, with such a name." He asked if I had ever met a girl named Gwynedd (pronounced Gwineth) but I had to tell him I did not. He gave up his pursuit of Welsh names then.

The Welsh are a devout, yet mischievous, people; they are wild, yet poetic; warlike, yet peace loving. And, as the world knows, they are melodious. In every city of Wales during the Christmas season, caroling is important — and beautiful. Almost everyone in town goes to the central city or market place to sing. Often contests are held to find the most beautiful music for a poem or a set of lyrics. By such a method, good songs and thrilling lyrics work their way inexorably into the musical culture of Wales. Few people sing so well — and so persistantly. The national spirit of Wales does not appear to be fading or dying out like its language; it is kept alive and vibrant by song.

Briefly and superficially I told him of my interest in Christmas customs in the world. He was prepared to present a long dissertation on the subject of the Welsh Christmas. I stopped him, however, on customs I had met elsewhere. The Welsh Christmas is similar to the English and therefore to the American Christmas. But I had not yet heard of Mari Llwd.

Gwynn told me what he knew about the ominous Mari

Llwd. He had seen it once when he was a young man. He had asked about it and wondered about it but the custom of having Mari Llwd during the Christmas festival had all but died from Wales.

Mari Llwd was a grotesque horse head, sometimes the actual horse's skull, and sometimes a wooden, burlesqued imitation. On St. Stephen's Day, December 26, it ran the streets threatening every passerby and making motions as if it was anxious to bite. Its jaws were moveable and when they were opened and closed they made a great clatter, Gwynn recalled.

The horse's head was attached to the end of a long pole. The other end of the pole was lashed to the chest of a young man who would travel on his hands and knees, now and then pulling a cord which would make the horse's jaws move. A large white cloth like a sheet would be thrown over him and he would go into the countryside and threaten to bite people. Once he had them at bay — and it was polite and politic to stay that way — the only method to achieve freedom was by paying a small fee in cash or cakes or cookies or a drink of some kind.

Gwynn's story was interesting to me; I had never heard of any such Christmas season custom. But it was once fairly common, he told me, in various countries.

"In the Hartz mountains a similar custom was practiced," Gwynn said. "The beast was called the Habersack. The youth beneath the white cloth held a forked stick instead of a pole. But a pole was laid, then tied, crossways to the fork of the stick to resemble horns. It was," said Gwynn, "a kind of a goat, a Yule goat."

My mind raced back to a visit I had had earlier with the Finnish Yulbuk — the Yule goat, Joulupukki. I wondered if there was some kind of association. But I dismissed the thought. I was unable to answer it in any event.

"And," said Gwynn, "in the Usedom Island there is another horselike creature of Christmas, the Klapperbach. And in some parts of Germany there is the Schimmel, also a white horse figure. There is, or was, also a Schimmel in Silesia, but this was managed with four or five young men, one of whom was called the Schimmelreiter. In Styria a long time ago, another such creature — this one another goat — roamed the country-side on St. Stephen's day. He was called the Habergaiss, and his main forte was to butt his head against children. Oh, yes, the Welsh Mari Llwd has had plenty of company."

Though we must guess that these dreadful figures date to the pre-Christian era and may have been associated with the pagans' sacrificial rites in which they slew their steeds and their goats to assuage the anger of their gods, such creatures as the Mari Llwd are strange manifestations.

The custom of playing the game with the horse's head or the goat's may have some vestigial association with St. Stephen, the first Christian Martyr. He was — according to legend — a man who loved horses. He had two roan horses, two whites and one dappled. It is put out that Stephen was murdered in a dark forest in Sweden, and that his body was tied to his horse which galloped home to Norrala. There St. Stephen was buried. Over his grave, in due time, a church was built. It was to this church, according to legend, that farmers brought their sick animals, especially their horses, on a pilgrimage for heal-ing. In Germany, St. Stephen's day is sometimes, and in some sections, called The Great Horse Day.

Gywnn remembered another animal of Christmas, a com-panion to Mari Llwd.

"The custom of using a horse's head during the Christmas season was also practised in early England, particularly in Cheshire. And what do you think they called *this* horse?"

I couldn't guess.

"Old Hob," said Gwynn. "Perhaps it is the source of the term, hobby horse."

I thought that it might well be. But I had become interested in my thoughts about the Yulbuk. I half wished I could talk to him again.

I heard a "whoosh!" Gwynn was gone, and so was I, with no time to thank him or say a polite goodbye. The Transvolo Stone had taken my half-formed wish and propelled me out of Wales. Where to this time?

12

IRELAND
AND OLD CUSTOMS

HEN I materialized, or seemed to, directly within view of a pretty, redheaded Irish girl in the strangely named village of Ballyjamesduff, I knew that I had mis-wished, or had expressed myself inadequately. I had wished to be in Finland, about 1,100 miles northeast of Wales. Instead, I had somehow arrived in Ireland which is scarcely 150 miles due west.

But adjustments could be made. Ireland is lush and green and beautiful, and the pretty girl who was staring at me was obviously frightened and needed to be reassured.

"I frightened you, didn't I," I said, lifting my hat.

"Indeed you did. Wherever did you come from?"

I avoided making an explanation although I had an interesting feeling that if I had explained, the pretty girl would have understood and believed. But I simply said that I had come from the United States. She already had guessed that. Americans are readily identifiable all over the world — by their speech, by their manners, by their dress, by their haircuts, by their shoes, and, very often, by the fact that they have a camera hung about their neck. I, however, had been whooshed away without mine.

She told me her name, Mary O'Neil, and I told her mine.

Then I explained my purpose and my wish to take part in some Christmas festivity peculiar to Ireland.

"You have come at the wrong time, sir. Else you would have the fun of Wren's Day, or First-Footing. Both are done here."

"What day is it?" I asked.

"Today is the 19th," said Mary O'Neil.

"Very well, I will wait for Wren's Day and First-Footing, whatever they may be."

"You're welcome in Ballyjamesduff," she said, "but a year is a very long time to wait for playing Christmas games."

"This is . . . January?" I asked, surprised.

"Indeed it is," she said with her strong and pretty Irish accent.

I explained that perhaps I could not wait. Would she be good enough to explain the Irish games?

We strolled through the village, with Mary O'Neil's bright, shining red hair gleaming in the slanting rays of the sunshine. As we walked I asked questions, but I also mused about my difficulty in navigating the courses over which the Transvolo Stone was sending me. My fault or the Stone's?

Mary pointed out her home as we walked, a pretty little stone house with whitewashed walls and a roof thatched with straw. The house, she said, was more than two hundred years old and she thought that members of her family had lived in it since it was erected.

Mary spoke English, of course, but she was also able to converse in Gaelic (sometimes called the Irish language) which is the traditional tongue of Ireland. Although Gaelic is a difficult language, Mary had learned it in school. The study of Gaelic is compulsory in all government-supported educational institutions in Ireland. Thus, Mary said, the chances of it dying away are remote. However, most Irish people speak English.

Mary chattered away so fluently that it amused me.

107

"Have you kissed the Blarney Stone?" I asked her.

She had, indeed.

"All Irish people wish to kiss the Blarney Stone," she said pertly, "but some of us do not need to."

Blarney is a town of County Cork in the Republic of Ireland. It grew up around Blarney Castle which was erected there in the middle of the 1400's.

High up on the castle wall is the Blarney Stone, an inscribed slab which is surrounded by legend. According to the story — and, surely it is the belief of every loyal Irishman — one who kisses the Blarney Stone is promptly endowed with the gift of eloquence and persuasive flattery. This is a country where it is scarcely needed!

Mary was well informed on her beloved country. She knew that St. Patrick is reputed to have brought Christmas to that island in the middle of the 5th century A.D.

"Patrick," she said, "gave Ireland its national symbol, the shamrock. He used the three-leafed plant to illustrate the Trinity. All Irish people love him and they love the shamrock too."

It did not seem polite or proper to explain to Mary that there is really no such plant as a shamrock. Botanically speaking, the shamrock does not exist. Some regard the wood sorrel as the true shamrock; others say it is the black medic; and still others identify the hop clover or the white clover as the proper one. "One would think that the Irish would get together and choose the proper plant to be the true shamrock, and then agree upon it, if the Irish ever agreed, but they do not," someone has said. Not I!

But the botanical species appears not to be important. Any trifoliate plant will do as the symbol of Ireland. It is just as well.

"Now, Mary, what really is Wren's Day and how did it begin?"

"I don't think anybody knows when it began, but all know it to be very ancient, dating back to the time before Jesus Christ." Mary nodded her head respectfully as most good Irish Catholics do when the name of the Son of God is mentioned. Mary kept chattering. A charming girl she was!

"On St. Stephen's day (December 26) the people of my village — and I daresay most other country towns — make an imitation wren from straw, or else acquire a proper stuffed one.

"They go from door to door of every house, and they sing a pert Irish song, one of the very well-known old ones. It goes like this," she said, and she lifted her pleasant voice in the ancient song:

> The wren, the wren, the king of all birds
> St. Stephen's day was caught in the furze.
> Although he is small, his family is great.
> Open up, lady, and give us a treat.

Furze is another name for gorse, common names for a thorny evergreen shrub native to Britain and western Europe.

"And does the lady of the house open the door and give the singers a treat?" I asked, pronouncing the word as Mary did.

"Indeed. She is expected to, and she does. The singers may do a bit of an Irish jig and sing another small song or two and they get their rewards, usually a sweet or a cookie. Then they move on to the next house."

"Do the singers leave the stuffed wren behind?"

"Oh, no! The wren is very precious. A long time ago — so my sainted mother told me — boys would kill wrens and use their little bodies to get their Wren's Day rewards. Now, though, if a boy has a live wren, he puts it in a cage and takes it 'round with him. He pretends that he is asking for a treat to feed the starving bird."

But nobody, Mary pointed out, knows whence came the

custom. It is safe to guess that the tradition is probably pre-Christian and related to the rites of sacrifice.

Mary said that all of the Irish people in her town put lighted candles in their front windows.

"It is a way to tell the passersby that they are welcome to this house," Mary said. "The Irish do not forget that Mary and Jesus were turned away when they were seeking lodging."

The game of First Footing was once a highly important rite which Mary thought was practiced in all of the British Isles. Based on pleasant superstition, it becomes important that the person who "first foots" or steps first into your house on Christmas morning is exactly the correct kind of person.

"It is important that the first guest has feet which water can flow under," Mary said.

I didn't understand.

"He must have well arched feet," Mary said, almost impatient with my thickness of mind. "Water can't flow under flat feet, now, can it?"

I thought not.

"Of course not. And the first one into your home must bring a present, perhaps even a lump of coal for the fireplace, or a stick, or a green pea — or anything of some value because it is a way to bring happiness and good fortune for the coming year."

"Anything else required of the first guest?"

"Yes. It is preferred that he or she have black hair — that is the best of good luck."

"Mary," I said, after I thanked her for the pleasant walk and the instructive talk, "if you came to my door with your beautiful red hair glowing as it does, I would count that very, very good luck."

Mary smiled sweetly and blew me a kiss as I walked away, and she called out after me, "Faith, and I wouldn't be doubting it if you had a bit of good Irish blood in you, Mr. American!"

I climbed up to a green, grassy knoll and tried hard to remember the proper words to use in my incantation. Then I asked the distant Transvolo Stone ("Pay attention, now!") to bring me home.

It did. But just before I heard the transportational sound of "whoosh," I heard Mary's plaintive voice call out, "Nodlaig mhaith agat!"

The Gaelic tongue is well suited for the calling of Merry Christmas. I think I have never heard the words sound so pretty.

13

CZECHOSLAVAKIA
AND THE DEMON CERT

HORTLY after I arrived home, I made my in-cantation at the Transvolo Stone. I appended an urgent request that I be allowed to visit Denmark or Finland. I was determined to keep trying. Then I waited.

My visitor arrived promptly but I was to wish that he had not. He was dressed in a black robe. His face was reddish in color. In one hand he carried a whip and in the other a length of chain. His appearance was so fierce and unsociable that I regretted my obligation to go and speak to him. But I did. (I entertained a thought that I might wish my neighbors would not see me in conversation with such a devilish looking creature.)

Approaching him, I spoke politely as I always try to do. I wished him a merry Christmas.

Up close, he was more horrible in appearance that he had looked as I peered at him from the window of my house. His teeth were prominent and sharp, and above his forehead he was equipped with a pair of short horns.

"Well," he said in a voice which was surprisingly pleasant, "how shall I return your greeting — in Slovakian? Stretan Bozic!"

"Thank you. Are you a Christmas figure?" I did not add the words "from Denmark or Finland" because he was clearly not from either place.

112

"I am from Ceskoslovenska. My name is Cert. Surely you have heard of me?"

I confessed that I had not. "Are you the helper to Santa Claus?" I asked.

"I know no such person. My duty is to accompany Svaty Nikalas when he comes to visit the children of Czechoslovakia (as you call it) on Svaty Nikalas Day, December 6. My principal function is to frighten little children, to remind them of what will happen to them if they misbehave."

He lashed out with his whip fiercely, cutting the air around him with such frenzy that I could tell he enjoyed his work. When he finished, he rattled the chains heavily and ominously. I did not think very much of him as a Christmas figure. Christmas, I told myself again, is a time of joy and happiness when the world is good and mankind loves mankind. I could not help it. I told my thoughts to my visitor. He was scowling as I tried to explain my feelings about being kind to children.

"Foolishness!" he said, his voice harder and crisper than it had been before. "Children should be obedient. If they have something to fear, like such a creature as I am, they tend to be silent and fearful of what may happen to them. I keep children good."

It was my turn to say "Foolishness." It angered him.

"Fear," he said, "is a wonderful weapon. It forces children to obey. And if they are not good, then they must be punished. And I do this. I like my work. I am the best helper that Svaty Nikalas could ever have."

"I don't think so," I said. "May I ask why you have come here? I had sent for someone from Denmark or Finland. You weren't even invited."

"Ah, that's the way of it, is it? I received the message but it came to me in Finnish. Naturally I went to Finland first, but some goat gave me trouble. Said I was trespassing, and that I should come to the United States."

"I wonder what happened that my message came to you."

"Well, it's perfectly clear to me. Somebody is scrambling your signals. When you asked your what's-its-name stone for Finland or Denmark, somebody jammed its system and mis-sent your message. It came straight to me, but it was a bit garbled." said Cert.

I wondered seriously about who would do such a thing. Who, I asked myself, would have anything to gain? Or was I being punished? These were questions I couldn't answer im-mediately. I turned to the present matter.

"As long as you're here, I don't want to seem unhospitable. Would you take me to your country to show me how Christ-mas is observed there?"

"Can't be done," he said with finality.

"And why can't it be done?"

"Well," he said, scowling, "along with the signal which came to me, there came a jolly voice which told me that if Finland tried to send me to the United States, I should not come. If I did, the jolly voice told me, and I tried to bring an outsider along, I would never be able to go back to my own country."

"And I am the outsider?"

"Obviously."

"Whose voice was this jolly one you speak of?"

"I think I recognized the voice of my boss. I must obey him."

"Svaty Nikalas?"

"The same."

It seemed to me that it is possible that Santa Claus of the U.S.A. might have a voice somewhat similar to the voice of Svaty Nikalas of Czechoslovakia.

"Well, then," I asked the Cert, "will you obey this order, or will you be frightened by the threat?"

"Of course I'll obey. It is *my* business to threaten and make people fearful in order to obtain their obedience. If I failed to obey somebody else, I would be guilty of hypocrisy. Hence, I will not take you to Czechoslovakia with me. It's that simple."

I saw no reason to argue with this creature.

"Will you sit here with me instead, and tell me something about the Christmas festival of Czechoslovakia?"

"Yes, for a little while. Then perhaps you might tell me something about your Christmas customs. Svaty Nikalas and I might like to move in here to sort of expand our territory. Ceskoslovenska is only about 450 miles long and 175 miles wide at the widest point. And, as you could guess, Svaty Nikalas and I, as well as some others, can cover this amount of geography easily enough. We have talked about taking over in your country."

"Frankly," I said, "I think such a Christmas creature as you would not be welcome here. We love our children. We do not like to frighten them into obedience. And, as for Svaty Nikalas, I don't know anything about him so I can't tell you if he would be welcomed by the people. However, I think that Santa Claus would do his best to prevent Svaty Nikalas from coming here."

"This Santa Claus — would he be the one who sent me the message?"

"I don't know. But the idea crossed my mind," I told him.

"What's he like?"

"He wears a red robe, white whiskers, and he is supposed to be a kind-hearted, benign gentleman filled with the milk of human kindness," I told him. "He lives at the North Pole except at Christmas time."

"Oh? Svaty Nikalas lives in heaven. When it is time for him to go gift giving on Svaty Nikalas Day, he comes down from heaven on a golden cord. An angel dressed in white comes along with him and I pretend that I do. I actually don't live in heaven, but when Svaty and the angel are part way down to earth, I get up there and join them in their descent."

"But you have Christmas December 6?"

"Well, we have the gift giving then, but we have what we call a first and second Christmas, December 25 and 26. Both days are national holidays, official ones. We all have the Christmas trees up by then, and there is some gift giving at that time, too."

"Do you have any special Christmas foods?" I asked.

"Yes. We have a special braided white bread called calta, or what you might call Christmas bread. One of our important streets in Prague is named Celetna which is the word calta is derived from. The reason is that once long ago many bakery shops were on that avenue. Our main dish is fish — carp. We always set one extra place at our Christmas tables. This is for the Christ Child, if He cares to join in for the dinner. And we are always careful in Ceskoslovenska to save a bit of each food item served at the Christmas table and see that the farm animals get their share. It leads to good luck during the next year."

"Those are very pleasant customs," I said.

116

"Of course," said Cert. He grinned and showed his sharp teeth. "We also have some of the neighbors dress as the Three Wise Men. They go around to the houses and sing songs. They're usually invited into the house for tea and cakes."

"All very good," I told him. "Many people pay a great deal of attention to the Magi."

"I know they do," said Cert, settling down a bit on the stone to get comfortable. "Can you tell me something about the Three Wise Men? They are a familiar sight in our country but I never learn much about them. They hardly speak to me." He said the last plaintively.

"You should really read the Bible" I told him. "Try Luke. He was a good reporter and told the story as well as it could be told. Matthew called them simply 'wise men from the east,' and he did not say that there were three of them. But by the eighth century, tradition had grown up around the story of the blessed Birth, and the wise men not only had names, but they had kingly titles—Melchior, Balthazar and Gaspar. The legend seems to have over-ruled St. Augustine who thought that there were twelve wise men, one for each of the twelve tribes of Israel.

"They were — these three men — rather strange kings. Obviously they had wealth for they brought gold and frankincense and myrrh. And they must have been wise men to openly acknowledge that someone could be wiser than they were. In those days, such a confession made by royalty would be at the risk of losing face."

I looked up at Cert who was relaxed and seeming to enjoy the discussion. My eye caught a movement at the far corner of my house. When I looked, I saw something bright red dodge back out of sight.

Cert had not seen the motion nor the flash of red. I decided to tell him. "Santa Claus is hiding over there."

Cert turned pale and then disappeared.

14

SANTA CLAUS COMPLAINS

ELL, thank you, Santa Claus — thanks a lot for chasing my guest away," I told him as he ambled up. I tried to put a great deal of sarcasm into my voice as I said it but I think I failed. Santa is, after all, a lovable fellow.

"You're welcome," he said, smiling. He believed he had really done me a favor!

"Yes. And thank you for scrambling the messages I sent out over the airwaves from the Transvolo Stone." This time I was able to sound sarcastic.

"You didn't like that?"

"Of course I didn't like that. I want to get to as many countries as I can. And, furthermore, I think it was you who bounced me around over there in Europe. I couldn't get where I wanted to go. I was even beginning to wonder if I was going to have to stay in the Soviet Union for the rest of my life."

"Oh, I was keeping my eye on things."

"You haven't been much help, Santa. You're causing me a lot of trouble. I really do want to study the Christmas customs of the world."

"Well, you see, that's what I don't understand," he said seriously. "Here you are with the best gift giver in the world and you want to go and study more of them. And where you ought to be interested in the Brownies who help me make the

118

toys for the children, you want to go abroad and study some of those horrible creatures."

"What horrible creatures?"

"Well, Cert from Czechoslovakia, for one. And Klaubauf in the Tyrol. And ugly Bartel, from Styria. You know the children don't leave cookies for him. They have to leave *schnaps*!"

"Well, if it's the custom of the country . . ."

"I'm trying to say that we should observe our own customs, not go dragging other people over here. I heard what Cert told you — that he and Svaty Nikalas were thinking about adding to their territory by moving into mine."

"It seems to me that we ought to consider all countries and their customs. Then we can bring the best customs to our land," I told him. I meant it, too.

"Do you think it would be nice to have monsters like Grampus from lower Austria here? Or Der Belsnickel which the Pennsylvania Dutch tried to foist off on me? Or a Billy Goat from Scandinavia? Or Shen Koll from who knows where? Or Black Peter from Holland? Or Mari Llwd from Wales"

I shrugged my shoulders.

"Maybe you'd like a woman gift giver like Befana from Italy, or an old hag like Babushka from the Soviet Union, or Berchtel from Swabia, or Budelfrau from Austria. Or maybe you'd rather have an ugly old woman like Buzebergt who hangs around Augsburg. That crowd? You'd rather have people like that than a jolly old Santa Claus and his sweethearted little Brownies?"

I couldn't say that I would. "But Santa, if you're as good as you say you are and as all of us think you are, you don't need to have any fear. We'd never let you go unless we found someone better."

119

"That's one of the troubles. You never know how people are going to react to anything these days. People are fickle, you know, and they are often unkind. After all the years I have served . . ." His voice faded away in self-sympathy.

"Santa," I said. "People are really very nice."

"Nice?" he said. "Yes, sometimes they are and then again sometimes they are not." He paused meaningfully "You know who St. Nicholas was?"

"Yes. He was the bishop of Myra, a very good soul. And you are created somewhat in his image. You should be proud of that."

"Not in his image, no. The bishop was a tall, thin man with a scraggly beard. When I was first created as a legend, I was tiny — a gnome, a mischief maker who also brought toys to good children. But as you say, I was somewhat patterned after St. Nicholas. My name is a version of his. Right?"

I agreed.

"Then all right. You know that St. Nicholas died on December 6, in about the year 343?"

"Yes."

"And was buried in his own church at Myra in Asia Minor?"

I nodded.

"And from that time his good deeds spread around the world? He became the patron saint of maidens, of children, of thieves, of sailors, of the Russian nation, and of a lot of other things?"

I agreed that this was so. "He is also the patron saint of pawnbrokers," I added, "and bakers, scholars, merchants, judges, travelers, murderers, innkeepers and paupers, and he is more widely venerated than any other saint except the Virgin Mary."

"That's right. He was buried in Myra in about 343."

"You said that, Santa."

120

"I wanted to repeat it. Is he buried there now?"

I said I thought he must be.

"No, he isn't. His bones had lain in the tomb at the church of Myra for 742 years, and people went there to pay homage to his memory."

It was taking Santa Claus a long time to make a point. I nodded wearily.

"You say people are always so nice. But in the year (about) 1085, some sailors and businessmen-merchants from the Italian city of Bari came and snatched his poor bones away from their burial place. They smuggled him out of there, their own patron saint, and they hauled him all the way to their hometown, the city of Bari down there at the heel of the Italian boot. And there in Bari they built a basilica and buried his bones. Do you think that was nice?"

I said it surely wasn't.

"But the people of Bari — every year on May 9, actually *celebrate* the theft! May 9 was the day the ships carrying the relics of St. Nicholas arrived home."

"It isn't nice of them. I'll agree to that. But I don't see what that has to do with my seeking Christmas customs in other lands and inviting representatives of other lands to come here," I told him.

"It has everything to do with it. I feel a positive affiliation with that noble man, and I know that if people would steal the bones of a wonderful man like St. Nicholas, they would also be perfectly willing to throw me out if the mood came to them. I wouldn't like that."

"They wouldn't throw you out, Santa. They all love you so much."

He tried not to look pleased, but he was. Yet he persisted.

"They threw out Grandmother Babushka, didn't they?"

"That was different, Santa. They discarded her because of

her association with the history of the church which the Soviet Union no longer officially accepts."

"I have noted changes in my day, too," he said, "which show that other peoples in the world have slacked up on their ideas because of religious reasons. For example," he went on, "there was a time when St. Nicholas Day was the day for me to give gifts. But today not many nations pay attention to Saint Nicholas Day, which is December 6. Once it was the most

remarkable children's festival of the year. But they forgot it in England and moved it up to Christmas Day. In Germany, at least in the northern parts, the Protestants stopped observing it because they thought it was too much like the practice of worshiping saints. Only in a few countries like Austria, Holland, Belgium, and Czechoslovakia and a couple of other places do they pay any attention to the day of St. Nicholas. You can't tell me that wasn't because of religious attitudes."

I couldn't and didn't. But I persisted in my right to visit other nations and seek out their ideas on Christmas customs.

Santa Claus was just as stubborn as I. "If you're so interested in other customs, why don't you just ask me? I'll tell you what they are and what I think of them."

I pointed out to him that his opinion was not objective and therefore of little value to me.

"I don't mind your going overseas," he said, "but I hate to have you bring that wild crowd over here where people can see them and think, 'Oh, boy, wouldn't it be nice to have a Christmas figure like that?' It could happen!"

I decided to let Santa Claus tell me about some of the customs in nations I was interested in. He's been spying on other nations for years.

"What kind of Christmas do they have in Scotland?"

"Why," he said with scarcely a thought, "the Scottish people are among the nicest people in the world, and among the most diligent and skillful. But their Santa Claus is a poor imitation of me. He's Father Christmas, a kind of a skinny fellow who doesn't laugh very much."

"Scottish people are described as 'dour,'" Santa went on. "Dour means . . ."

"I know what it means, Santa Claus," I told him. The word angers me a little bit because I have some Scottish blood. "It means, hard, stern and severe. But it isn't true. Scottish people are among the best, most loyal people in the world."

Santa Claus agreed. "But in general, Scottish people are not fond of religious festivals. Oh, they put up Christmas trees and they play first-footing, and they give gifts to their children, and up in the Highlands they sing carols."

I asked for an example. He sang a very old Scottish Christmas song:

> Sing hey the gift, sing ho the gift.
> Sing ho the gift of the living.
> Son of the Dawn, Son of the Star,
> Son of the Planet, Son of the Far,
> Son of the Planet, Son of the Far,
> Sing hey the gift, sing ho the gift.

The old chantey did not make much sense to me, but many ancient songs have obscure meanings. At any rate, I was pleased to hear the song. It reminded me that I knew an un-Christmasy one which I learned from some Scottish sailors, and which I liked. I sang it for Santa:

> I belong to Glasgee (Glasgow),
> Dear-r-r-r Old Glasgee toune.
> A-wha's a ma' 'er wi' Glasgee
> Cause it's goin' rooond and roooned.
> I'm only a common ol' wor-r-rkin' lad
> As innyone her-r-re can see;
> Bu' when oi've 'ad a cu' 'le o' d-ri-nks on a Sa'urdy
> Glasgee belongs to me!

"Very amusing," he said.
"Yes, I think so, too."
We both fell silent for a few moments. Then Santa Claus said, "Let's continue with our discussion. What other country would you like to know about?"

"Well, France, for one. Does France have a version of Santa Claus?"

"A rather poor copy, a sort of combination of Father Christmas and the thin man at the carnival shows. They call him Père Noël which is the French way, of course, of saying Father

124

Christmas. He has a helper, too — le compagnon de Père Noël —whose name is Père Fouettard."

"Is he a nice fellow?" I asked.

"Well, he's an informer. If a little boy or little girl does something naughty, Père Fouettard goes and snitches on him to Père Noël. You know, of course, that there is another Fouettard — the one from Belgium. I believe you have made his acquaintance."

"Indeed I have," I said, and I rubbed my stomach remembering the blow he had struck there. "Is the French Foeuttard a Spanish moor?"

"The French do not consider him to be, but he is quite an angry fellow, much more unpleasant than my jolly little Brownies. He is stern and full of discipline, and he is the one who reminds Papa Noël just exactly how each child has behaved during the past year. He remembers all too well. In fact, when Père Noël places the Christmas presents under the tree, Père Fouettard places little bunches of birch twigs, all wrapped in pretty ribbons, right alongside the gifts."

"What meaning have they?"

"They mean what you think they mean — they're reminders that naughty children may get spanked with them."

"It somehow doesn't seem as nice as your way, Santa," I said. "I would think the thought of the birch rods would destroy some of the joy of getting presents."

"Exactly. That is why I don't understand why you want to bring that crowd over here."

"I keep telling you that they'd never replace you — not in this country."

"Don't be so sure. I remember that one time in . . . let's see, I think it was Portugal . . . they tried to kick their Père Noël out and supplant him with a more recognizable giver of gifts. They used him for a few years. Called him Father Indian, for goodness' sake! But he didn't last long; Père Noël was asked to come back. They had to beg him."

"About France. When do the children have their Christmas?"

"St. Nicholas Day, December 6, is very important in some places, especially in Lorraine. According to an old belief among the French, the Virgin Mary once gave Lorraine to St. Nicholas as a reward for his kindness. That's why what they call La Saint Nicolas (the feast of St. Nicholas) is important there; and some of its importance has been drawn to other communities. So, for the French children, St. Nicholas Day is the beginning of Christmas. Father Noël visits the homes on St. Nicholas Eve and puts presents in the children's shoes. When they go to bed, they say a little prayer asking that Papa Noël will be good to them. They say,

> Saint Nicolas, mon bon patron,
> Envoyez-moi quelqu'chose de bon.

The children get candies and nuts and things like that; not nearly as much as I bring them, that is, in the United States."

"Well, it's really the spirit of giving that counts, Santa. Not the amount or the size of the pile."

"I agree but I try to be generous."

"Then, if the children get their gifts on St. Nicholas Eve, what happens Christmas Eve?" I asked him.

"That's what the French call La Veille de Noël. It is a time for devotions, for attention to the crèche which is in almost every French family. But Church bells ring at midnight in a joyous way to announce the birth of Christ and the time for Christmas mass. Then, after mass, the French usually hold family parties in which a late supper is served. At this meal, goose is served by families in many parts of the country. They say that the reason for serving a goose dinner is because the geese welcomed the Wise Men as they approached the stable where the Child Jesus lay."

126

"It seems to be small thanks — to the geese," I said. But I didn't mean it.

"Then," Santa continued, "the children expect another visit from the gift giver. In some places, it is le Père Noël and in others the gifts are thought to come directly from le petit Jésus. The next day, Christmas—or Noël, as they term it—is a time for family dinners and exchanging gifts. A rather nice Christmas, I must say, wrapped as it is in religious rites and staying all pretty well within the family. If it has any weakness, I would say that it is the rather thin fellow who poses as Père Noël, and his unpleasant assistant."

"I suspect that the children of France love him as much as the children here love you. Are there any other rites in France, like first footing or that business about the wren?"

"Well, not any more. But it is a pretty thing to know that in some parts of France, the little wren is looked upon with much affection. It is called Poulette de Dieu because the wren is supposed to have brought soft feathers and moss to make a little blanket for le petit Jésus."

"A tender thought," I said.

Santa had apparently exhausted his knowledge of the French Christmas customs for he volunteered no more. I waited a moment and then, boldly, I made my statement.

"I want to go to Finland or Denmark because I owe it to those people. I hope you will do nothing to keep me from either of those places. I must insist upon my rights."

"I withhold my judgment on what is right to do," he said after a pause filled with petulance. "I can tell you all you need to know about those places. And I don't think I'd care to have you bring a goat to parade around in my country and threaten my very existence."

"We've been all through that, Santa. I know what I want to do and I am going to do it. I will be happy if you do not jam my signals at the Transvolo Stone. Apparently you can send me elsewhere, but I suspect that you do not have the power to keep me home or to keep guests out of this country." I spoke sternly, but I believe that I was correct.

He pouted.

"Now listen," he said at last, trying appeasement. "I don't mind it when you go abroad and I hope that you enjoy yourself while doing it. But I don't like to have you bring spies into my territory, and I don't enjoy having you bring back customs that might tend to pre-empt me here. I have been a good and loyal servant and . . ."

"Oh, Santa!" I said. "We've been over that again and again."

Without another word, Santa Claus stood up, tugged on his whiskers and walked away in stiff-backed anger.

15

VENICE
AND A GONDOLIER

TRIKE while the iron is hot," is an old saying which my grandmother used often when I was a boy. It seemed to fit as a timely bit of advice, as did "Suit the action to the word," "A stitch in time saves nine," and "Action is the child of thought." Hence I acted.

I addressed myself to the Transvolo Stone even before Santa Claus was out of sight. I asked to go to either Finland or Sweden.

I went into the house and dressed as warmly as I could, and then I waited. When I glanced out of the window a few minutes later, I was confounded. Sitting there, just as before, was the old woman of Russia, Babushka. Santa was certainly dedicated in his opposition.

I walked out and gave her my greeting in English.

"Merry Christmas, Babushka!" I was determined to be polite even though I was disappointed.

"I understand the first two words," said my visitor, speaking (I thought) Italian, "but I do not understand why you call me babushka. It is a kind of a headkerchief, is it not?"

"It is your name. Your own name!"

"Nonsense," she said in a hoarse, cackling voice. "My name is Befana."

129

"I have heard that name before, Madame," I said. "Are you from Italy?"

"I am. My name is a corrupted form of the Italian word, Epifania, meaning Epiphany."

I knew that Epiphany is a feast celebrated January 6 to commemorate the coming of the Magi as being the first manifestation of Christ to the Gentiles.

"Would you prefer me to address you as Epiphania? I would like to show my respect to you by not becoming too familiar."

"No, Befana is quite satisfactory. I am called nothing else. You are a very polite young man," she said. "Are all Americans like you?"

"I think our instincts are to be kind, and kindness is a form of courtesy, isn't it?"

"Of course. Well, I am delighted to be here. I have been wanting to pay a visit to this country since the territory was taken over by that young fellow you have here. His name?"

"Santa Claus. But, Befana, we are very fond of him. We would not like to have anybody replace him, not even you." I said the last with a shudder.

"But of course you would like me here. I understand he is a large, obese fellow who can hardly get around his territory on the celebration of the Gesù Bambino's birth."

"He has a large territory, I grant you, but he is quite able to make his rounds. He travels by reindeer, in the sky."

"It's one of the reasons I would like to come here to live and to stay. I must do all of my traveling on foot. I do get rather tired."

"I'm afraid I do not know what your duties are, Befana," I told her. "Nor how you function during the Christmas season."

"Oh. I thought everybody knew that. Well, on Epiphany Eve I go around and give presents to the children. Epifania is the time for gift giving."

"I am a little surprised to see a woman serving as a sort of Italian Santa Claus," I pointed out. "How did it ever happen that you were given such duties?"

"Shall we get one thing straight at the beginning?" she asked. "I am not serving, as you say, as a sort of Italian Santa Claus. Santa is serving your people as a sort of American Befana. So much for that. My story is very old and my duties came to me even before Santa Claus was a little boy.

"A long time ago I lived in a little cottage along the great highway where the camel caravans passed. I had lost my child and my husband to the plague. I was lonely and sad, but I wanted to get by as well as I could, and to mind my own business. Then, one day when I was very busy with my housework some unusual looking men in a camel caravan stopped at my door and spoke to me in a language I didn't understand. I was told later that all they were doing was asking me the way to Bethlehem. Well. I had never heard of Bethlehem!

"These men were dressed in fancy robes, like kings, and they wore crowns, like kings. They said something about a Bambino, but how was I to know what they meant? The caravan was long and there were many riches among the people in it, I could see that. And they talked and talked and they seemed excited, as if some really wonderful thing had happened. They invited me to go along, but it was getting on toward nightfall and I feared the dark and I did not think I should go with such foreign looking people.

"I told them that I didn't wish to go with them, and they moved on toward a great, shining star in the sky.

"The next day a shepherd came and told me who those men were. He urged me to follow them, but I was afraid to. I wanted to go and see the wonderful Bambino, but it is always difficult for me to look at a child and not have sad thoughts about my own. I thought it over again and again and finally

131

I decided that I would go to this place, this Bethlehem. And I got together some of the things my own baby had had.

"I wanted to give them to the sweet little Child the shepherd told me about, and I started out. But I could not find the foreign men, and I did not know where Bethlehem was. So I wandered and wandered and night came and I could not find them."

Befana looked so sad that I reached over and patted her shoulder sympathetically. I saw now that she was not an ugly hag as I had first thought. Deep within her there was great goodness, and it showed through the old face and the deep wrinkles.

I thought quietly that this wonderful old woman would make a fine helper for Santa Claus, or — even — a substitute for him when he was busy with other things. Then I felt ashamed. I was thinking the very thoughts that Santa Claus objected to! I was being disloyal.

Befana sighed, then continued.

"And that is about the entire story. Because I refused to accompany these strange looking foreign men, I must do penance. Italian people say that is my work for ever and ever to go forth on Epifania to search for the Christ Child. And I do, but I have not found him in almost two thousand years. Do you think that some day I might?"

"I do think that, Befana," I told her. But of course I could not know any such thing.

There was a long, long pause. Then she seemed to brighten.

"You sent for me. I received the message in a strange language and I thought perhaps that I was being summoned by one of those foreign men. I know, of course, that I am not being invited as I once was, but you called me and I let myself come to where I was told to come. What do you wish?"

"I wish to go to your country with you so I can observe how the Christmas season comes about there," I said.

I added that I was sorry the message came to her in a foreign tongue, but that I wasn't able to send the message properly due to interference of some kind. I hoped that she would not discover the inhospitable attitude of the American Befana. I blushed when that terminology came to me. I had really meant our very own Santa Claus.

She stood and indicated that she was ready to go.

"Where to?" I asked. "A little fishing village, or a mountain town, or a great city like Florence?"

"I thought you might like the romance and the history of Venezia."

"Venezia?"

"Yes. You call it Venice, I think."

I was delighted, then gone. After the familiar sound of "whoosh" I found myself with Befana, who was now invisible to the people of Venice, standing in the Piazza of St. Mark, a breathtakingly beautiful place with two most imposing buildings on the eastern end — the Church of St. Mark and the Doge's Palace.

I remembered something that Napoleon had said: "This is the most beautiful square in the world, and the sky is its ceiling."

I did not at first notice the smiling man standing nearby and staring at me. I looked, observed his excited interest, and smiled. He strolled over, offered his hand, and said, "I am Giuseppe Montagnaro and I perceive you are admiring our beautiful piazza. I know you are an American and I welcome you. Can I do anything to make your stay more pleasant?"

I told him of my hopes.

"Excellent! You shall come and stay with me and my family."

I was to learn that Giuseppe is a Venetian gondolier, a very proud gondolier for, he said, "One cannot be a gondolier until his father has been one."

I murmured politely.

"Is it not wonderful that my father was a gondolier, and that his father was before him, and his father and his father back a thousand years? One must be proud of this, no?" he said.

Giuseppe is 31 years old and has three children — bambinos — and his gondola which he also speaks of as his child. It weighs about a thousand pounds and is about thirty-five feet long. Its stern leans to one side, the better to give him an advantage of leverage when he leans upon his long, single oar.

"My gondola, like all of them here, is made by hand and has not changed in form for more than a century. I have seen pictures or drawings of gondolas a thousand years ago, and they were very like the one I have today."

He was very proud that his father and three brothers are gondoliers, too, and that all the male members of his family will become gondoliers when the time is right. And that, he said, does not come when they are of age, but only when an opening occurs — when another gondolier retires or dies.

His income, he told me, is about $2,350 per year, and that is a good wage in Venice.

Giuseppe showed me how to propel his beautiful boat through the waters of Venice (there are 760 canals through the ancient city). The boat, which has a capacity load of nine people, is thrust forward by a single long oar which fits into a tough, knotty wooden device called the "forcola" or fork which is hand made. The gondolier leans firmly and heavily on the handle of the long oar, then feathers the blade as he prepares for the next forward stroke. A very good, very strong gondolier can speed some seven miles in 35 minutes, if he would be permitted to in those congested waters. There are 450 gondolas in Venice, 50 of which are privately owned.

The 50 privately owned gondolas belong to wealthy people who keep their own gondola-chauffeur. The others are owned by individual gondoliers who are in business like Giuseppe, or by a franchised company much in the manner of an American taxicab firm.

"Do you sing when you travel the canals with your passenger?" I asked him.

"Yes, if they ask that I do so, or if I sometimes have two-three glasses of wine — then I sing as I go. I do not of my own wish sing what Americans think of as a good Venetian song — 'O Sole Mio.' I prefer to sing 'Racconta un Gondolier' but I will sing the other if it requested."

"Why is every gondola painted black?" I asked him. "Surely it would be beautiful if they were painted gay, happy colors, would it not?"

"Sì," he said, and he laughed gaily. "The reason is more than 200 years old. There was a Venetian doge at that time — a doge was a chief magistrate in Venice long ago, like a governor, and they were very powerful. In those days, all gondolas were painted as the owner wished to have them — red or blue or green or a mixture of colors. But the doge was a villain. As he was rowed from one gambling house or another in the early morning, the townfolks grinned at him, knowing very well that he had been up to no good. When his gaily painted gondola swam outside an unsavory place, all the Venetian world would know of his visit. It was all too easy to identify the official gondola. The doge had his gondola painted black. But still people knew. It was the only black one! Then he changed all that. He passed a law which demanded that every gondola on the canals of Venice be painted black. And black they have been to this day!"

Befana, invisible to Giuseppi, cackled. She liked the tale.

Giuseppe lived on a little back street in an apartment house built on poles sunk into the bottom of the canal. The structure tilted and would soon need some more work to keep it from sinking to the bottom of the canal.

"Always, always must this be done with every building in Venice," he explained, "or they will sink. Our beautiful city is situated on 120 islands formed by 177 canals in the lagoon between the mouths of the Po and the Piave rivers at the north end of the Adriatic Sea. Have you heard that our city is often called The Queen of the Adriatic?"

I nodded. "You have a railroad here, though. It isn't all water transportation?"

"Sì. The railroad connects our city with the Italian mainland, but there are no automobiles nor anything else of that kind in our city. They are against the law. Almost everything, except the railroad, of course, moves over the water. We walk many places. There are about 400 bridges in our city, but all buildings are on pile foundations which keep sinking deeper and deeper into the water. Some day there will be no Venezia," he said sadly.

Tradition has it, Giuseppe told me, that Venice was founded in the year 452 when some people of northern Italy took refuge on the islands to hide from the marauding barbarians who invaded Italy. By the year 991, Venice was the greatest center for trade to and from the east, and at last it became the strongest, richest power in the region of the Mediterranean. After the attacks by the Turks in the 15th century, and the years of invasions by other foreign powers, its importance declined. In 1797, Napoleon put an end to the Venetian Republic and it ultimately became part of Italy.

Giuseppe's wife, Maria, and their three children were hospitable, and they gesticulated with their hands almost con-

136

stantly as they talked as most good Italian people do. The motions were so fluid and graceful that I found conversing with them a delight, for with their hands they made nuances of added expressions and gave accent and visual meaning to the words as they spoke. I am now surprised that other peoples do not add more charm to speech by the arts of gesticulation.

The children were smaller for their age than American children are, and they were black-eyed, dark-haired and charming. There were the boys, Giovanni and Elio, and the daughter, Angelina, who volunteered to tell me about Christmas in Italy.

In that country, as in some others, Santa Lucia (St. Lucy) is much venerated on her day, December 13. Her fiesta on that day is observed with bonfires and torchlight parades and great displays of illumination. Santa Lucia really has two fiesta days, the other one on the first of May. But lights and illuminations are important because, it is said, she was blinded on the shortest and darkest day of the year. Santa Lucia is patroness of people who suffer diseases of the eye, and she is surely one of Italy's most beloved saints.

La Befana? The children knew her story well. Elio said that he remembered one time at Epifania when La Befana came to his bed with a lighted candle and looked long into his face to see if he, perchance, was the Gesù Bambino.

"She seemed to sigh when she saw that I was not," said Elio, "and she turned sadly and walked from the room."

I looked at the Befana, not seen by the others. She nodded.

There was no Christmas tree in the household, for trees are a rarity in Venice; but there was a beautiful Christmas crib in a central place in the main room of the house. Called a "presepio" rather than a French crèche or American crib, or the German krippe, it is one of the most important Christmas decorations in an Italian home. Giuseppe's was, he said, more than a hundred years old and had been handed down to him by his father. Handmade and artistic, each of the figures was dressed in splendid clothes, all made by hand with painstaking care.

During the Christmas season the presepi are everywhere; and every church exhibits its version of what a presepio ought to be, and they are magnificent, some of them so large as to

138

fill a huge room. Perhaps because Italians have a greater love for children than most other people, the presepio with the Christ Child is more thoroughly used than in almost any other place.

Another reason for its almost excessive popularity may be the legend that St. Francis instituted the custom at Greccio, as mentioned earlier, in the year 1224. It is, however, a legend. Though the good saint of Assisi may have popularized the custom of the presepi, there is ample evidence that Pope Gregory III who lived in the sixth century was fond of presepi and had one placed in the early 700's in the church of Santa Maria in Rome. There are numerous earlier instances of the use of the manger scene. It was not introduced by St. Francis.

Befana sat nodding. It was clear that she enjoyed listening to stories about Christmas customs. Sometimes she smiled softly to herself. She appeared to be sleeping but she was not.

Christmas in Italy, I learned quickly from my new friends, is a religious festival. It commences with a novena, a nine-day period of devotional preparation, and a twenty-four hour fast, from sunset of December 23 to sunset of Christmas Eve (La Vigilia).

On each morning throughout the novena, most Italian families pray before the presepio and light candles. But Christmas Eve becomes a time for family gatherings and a cenone — a festive, meatless supper in which eels are served, large sized eels called capitoni. Christmas Day is always a sacred holiday in Italy, filled with prayers and devotions and then quiet family gatherings at home.

La Befana listened to the discussions and kept nodding her head. Now and then she looked sharply toward me as though something was not right. Still invisible to our hosts, she now placed her hands over her ears and gave me a look of dismay. Then she gestured wildly for me to leave the house. I took many moments to say my goodbyes to these good Italian people.

Outside, Befana told me that some strange, fierce noises were belaboring her ears.

"The language is English," she said, "but I do not understand it. The messages are coming louder and louder. Perhaps it means that you are being summoned. The noises and the calls are similar to the ones I heard when you summoned me to the Transvolo Stone.

"Perhaps," she added as an afterthought, "it is your American Befana who is calling you back."

I thanked the Befana for her kind help. I also apologized for thinking of her earlier as an ugly witch. She nodded, and gave me a "Buone Feste Natalizie." I made my wish. Then I whooshed.

16

TERRITORIAL EXPANSION

HE MOMENT I materialized in my back yard adjacent to the Transvolo Stone I saw the reason for the garbled, impassioned messages which La Befana had intercepted. Santa Claus was there in great disputation with a goat-like creature I recognized as the Joulupukki, or Julebok, or Yulbuk, of Finland. Standing nearby with baleful looks and his ever-ready pike pole was Père Fouettard of Belgium. It appeared to be a three-way quarrel.

As I appeared, Santa Claus turned to me.

"See what you have done? These creatures — this goat-man or whatever he is, and this punisher of children — have decided that they ought to come over here and help me distribute Christmas gifts."

Santa was quite perturbed and I did not blame him.

"Gentlemen," I said, addressing myself to the foreign visitors, "Santa Claus has managed to function with great efficiency here, never ever forgetting good children, and with a great deal of help from his Brownies. I am pleased that you would come and pay us a friendly visit, but now I must ask how you got here. I am going to ask you, also, if you will please leave."

The Joulupukki snorted. "The air waves of the nations are in an uproar due to some misuse of this silly rock here, and because someone has been jamming the transmission of messages. I had to come; I couldn't help it. And I am going to stay."

Père Fouettard, in his Spanish accent, was peppery and un-friendly. "I gave you reason once not to toy with me," he said as he indicated his stout pole. "And I am quite able to swing it again — either at you or at Mr. Chubby here."

I was horrified. I had never heard Santa addressed with such disrespect. "That is a show of very bad manners," I said to Père Fouettard. "You have no right to speak of Santa Claus this way; he is a fine, good man and we are quite happy with his work. The only reason you were invited here was to teach me something about how you spend your Christmas, both of you. We are not looking for a replacement nor a helper for Santa Claus."

"Tull og Toys!" said Joulupukki, a phrase he had used earlier to express his feelings that nonsense was being bandied about. "I have decided to spend my Christmases here, and I need no help from either Santa Claus or this fellow here," and he jerked an unfriendly thumb toward the black-faced man from Belgium.

142

Père Fouettard, always too ready with his stick, lifted it above his head and walked toward the goat-man. I decided that this had gone far enough. I stepped on the Transvolo Stone and made a wish that our guests go back where they had come from. I was just in time. As Père Fouettard was de-materializing, he threw his stout club at the Joulupukki with terrible swiftness, but it sailed through thin air as the goat-man, too, disintegrated and was gone.

Santa heaved a sigh and sat down heavily on the Transvolo Stone.

"I'm sorry," I told him. "I wouldn't want you to have such an experience for anything. It was all very distasteful."

"For you it was distasteful," he said morosely, "but for me it was torture. I have been trying to pacify those creatures for the past three hours. It has been anything but pleasant for me, I will tell you that." He sighed again, then looked at me. "Why do you persist in doing this?"

"All I wanted was to find out how other people have their Christmas," I said. "It was you who jammed the airwaves and scrambled messages."

"I'll admit to doing that. But you must remember that all I am trying to do is protect my territory. And I must say that the Transvolo Stone requires some delicate understanding and manipulation. I don't quite see how it works. But," he said as he looked at me fiercely, "I told you that if you wanted to learn anything about other countries, you should ask me. I know how that crowd does things. I can explain it to you. You don't have to go and invite them into my territory, and you don't have to pay them a visit. I know all about them."

"Santa, I don't see how you can be so jealous of your territory as you call it. It isn't really your territory. It was here long, long before you came. Besides, when you tell about the other countries, you are not objective. You try to find fault. You know, there is something lacking in everybody. Nobody is perfect."

Santa looked horrified. "Well, that is the first time anybody ever told me that I am not perfect. I try so hard, I am so loyal . . ."

"Please, not again!"

"Well, I do. So if you don't think I'm perfect, then I suppose I am terrible — maybe worse than Fouettard or Berchtel or Grampus or Budelfrau or Pelznickle, or Klaubauf even. Oh, I guess I must be a horrible person to be classed with that crowd!"

"Now you know very well that I don't think you are horrible, and I most certainly did not class you with those other people. You're a very, very good man, very kind and jolly."

"Good looking, too?" he asked. "Do you think I have a rather pleasant appearance? Superior, say, to the Dutch Sinterklaas?"

"Very much so," I said. "Very, very much so."

He stroked his beard for a moment and turned to me with a friendly smile.

"All right. What do you want to know? What country are you interested in? I will tell you whatever you want to hear about."

I felt that I had to appease him. I had caused him much trouble and unhappiness and I perceived now that it would be best if I engaged him in a conversation about other places.

"I would like to know how Finland celebrates Christmas. I have asked to go there, but I have been repeatedly rejected."

"I know all about Finland," said Santa. "The Finnish people really love Christmas and they practice it very nicely." He glanced sideways at me and added in a lower tone, "Of course, I don't think they do it quite as well as we do in my territory. But never mind . . . Have you ever heard of a sauna?"

"It's a kind of a steam bath?"

"Yes. Just before Christmas Eve, practically everybody in Finland takes a steam bath. Stones are kept in a little house in the backyard, and these are heated by fire for hours before one enters the bath house. The men bathe first, going into the hot little room and dashing cold water upon the stones to make them steam. It is sometimes so hot and steamy in the little bath house that people have trouble drawing a deep breath. When the men are well steamed and covered with perspiration, they run out of doors and roll in the snow. Then, to stimulate the circulation, they take a handful of thin branches and they lash each other smartly enough to turn the skin red!"

It doesn't matter, though, Santa pointed out. The hardy Finns love the sauna and they are sure that it is healthful, cleansing, and the proper way to take a bath. When the men and the boys have finished, the women and the younger children follow. Then it is time to eat.

"I would think that they would be hungry, Santa," I said, and I knew that such a steam bath is relaxing. But the meal for the occasion is not huge; it is sensible. Typical is barley porridge mixed with almonds, cream, and sugar, followed by fish and prune cakes.

"Is that enough of Finland's Christmas customs? They really do many of the same things we do in our country — put up a Christmas tree, go to church Christmas morning, and things like that," Santa said.

But I wondered about the *different* customs. I asked about them.

"Oh, well," Santa said, "everybody observes Christmas in his own way. The Finns are hardy, devout, church-going. Almost all of the population of Finland belongs to the Evangelical Lutheran Church."

"I know Finns are hardy people," I told Santa, "but have they been living as they do — so competent and strong — for a very long time?"

"Well, I don't know too much about the background of the people," he said, "but I know Christianity reached there in about 1157 when King Eric of Sweden led a crusade to Finland and conquered the Finnish tribes. He brought Christianity with him then. They are a remarkable people, and there is music in their hearts. One of the greatest Finns was the composer, Jean Sibelius, who composed the country's most beautiful orchestral music, the tone poem *Finlandia*.

"Oh, yes," Santa added, "The Finns are a strange and remarkable people. Their name probably is derived from the Latin word, *Fenni*, which means 'people of the fens' or the marshes or bogs. Their own name for their country is *Suomen Tasvalta* which translates to 'Land of a Thousand Lakes.' Finns speak of themselves as *Suomi*."

"The gift giver, I suppose, is the Joulupukki," I said. "I must admit that he doesn't seem to have your gentle manners."

"Thank you," Santa said. "The Julebok, as he is sometimes called, is the prime giver of gifts. But in some parts of Finland, the gifts come from an old man with a huge, long mustache which is pure white. He wears a white hat with blue bands upon it, and his usual costume is a long red coat. His name is Wainamoinen."

To my surprise I heard a sudden, soft sound behind me. I turned at the same time Santa turned. There, sitting behind me on the Stone was the person Santa had just described. I stared and, from the corner of my eye, I observed Santa scowling fiercely.

"Iloista Joulua!" said the visitor in a cheery voice. His mustache was of the handlebar variety and each side was at least two feet long!

When Santa did not return his Christmas greeting, I spoke for both of us. "Merry Christmas, Wainamoinen!"

146

He leaned back and surveyed my backyard. "A very nice country you have here," he said. " I trust there is room in such a great country for a fellow like me?"

Santa sputtered but said nothing.

Wainamoinen seemed to be ignoring him. "I overheard some of your conversation," he said. "While on my way here in answer to some kind of strange summons, I stopped for lunch in Lithuania. Would you like to hear about it?"

Out of deference to Santa's feelings, I did not respond. But the new guest took our silence to mean that we wanted to hear his story.

"I was invited to a Lithuanian home through my Finnish friend, Kauko Maki, who was unable to join me because he has not the flying power. But I stopped at the Lithuanian home only long enough to say hello to Kauko's friends there, the Antanas Dambrauskas family, and to have lunch on a table covered with straw.

"Straw?" I asked the question in spite of my will to remain silent. Santa gave me an angry nudge as though to say, "Don't encourage him!"

"Yes, straw. The entire tabletop was covered with straw to remind the Lithuanians of the manger which was the birth-place of Jesus. Do you know that story? Well, we had a huge, lunch which they themselves call *lietuva*. There were mush-rooms, tiny loaves of poppy seed bread, fish, a mixture of oil and more mushrooms, chicken, and sweet candies. I was sorry that I had to obey the command to come here."

"You weren't commanded to come," Santa said with a cer-tain coldness in his voice.

"Oh, but I was," said Wainamoinen with sarcasm. "I dis-tinctly heard my name called by the Great Santa Claus. How could I resist?"

"I didn't call your name; I pronounced it. I was explaining to this gentleman that you are sometimes the gift giver of

Finland in certain places. You may leave anytime you wish."

"Well, I rather like it here. I cover only a very small portion of a very small country. There are so many lakes there — 60,-000 when I last counted them — and they cover up a great deal of land. Hence I can usually finish my gift giving in a relatively short time. I could quite easily sail right over here and take up the duties of gift giving in this country. Not a bad thought, eh?"

Santa Claus cleared his throat and was about to make a comment, an unfriendly one, I guessed. But at that second we heard a remarkable succession of sounds just above our heads. The strange noises were similar to the sound of birds in flight. Wainamoinen paid them no attention whatsoever, but Santa seemed to be perturbed.

"Whatever was that noise?" I asked nobody in particular.

"Oskereien," said Wainamoinen with a diffident manner.

I looked in amazement at Santa Claus. "What in the world are Oskereien?" I asked him.

Speaking sotto voce, he said, "They're scamps of the Norwegian countries, tiny unblessed ogres and goblins who fly through the night and do mischief and damage during the Christmas season."

Leaning back indolently and almost disrespectful of Santa's presence, Wainamoinen added, "They can do no damage in the daytime. At night, however, they try to carry people off with them to wherever it is they go. They can fly faster than a thousand miles and hour, and they are so small that they cannot be seen while flying at such a speed. Want to see how they look?"

Without waiting for an answer, he waved his arm in a beckoning gesture. Almost instantly the air was filled with the sound of feathered wings. Then, to my dismay, thousands of tiny men about the size of small birds, settled down around

148

us, and even upon us. Their tiny voices were high and piercing and uncomfortable to my ears. I could not understand their language if, indeed, they were speaking. It sounded rather more as if they were jabbering gleefully. At least a dozen of them settled on both Santa and me, though they left Wainamoinen alone. Santa and I pushed them off. He was sorely troubled. I could see it in his face.

"What do they want?" I directed the question to Santa, but our Finnish visitor answered.

"They came at my bidding," he said. "I know you would like to learn about how other countries celebrate the Christmas festival. Well, these little people fly so swiftly that they can dart away, get an answer to a question and return almost as quickly as your Santa What's-his-name can answer. Want to see 'em work?"

I had been looking at the tiny men. They were dressed somewhat alike, but in different colors, mainly reds and blues and greens; they wore polka dots, stripes, zig-zag patterns and solid colors. Each wore a little green scarf and each had a small white beard. And all of them jabbered continuously.

"Well?" Wainamoinen said. "How about the Netherlands?" He said something unintelligible but apparently understood by the Oskereien. Several hundreds of them flew off, and in seconds they looked like a single gray streak in the sky.

"You shall see how Europeans function. We pride ourselves on our efficiency. I think that you would find if I were to take over the duties of the . . . the older gentleman there . . . you would be very happy with my work. I rather like it here in your country. Everbody is so polite."

"Thank you. We are content with the way we do things."

"No, you are not! Else why would you wish to study the methods of other peoples at the Christmas period? If you were content, you would leave well enough alone."

Santa nodded glumly to this statement, then he turned and glared at me.

Before I could respond to either the statement or the glare, there came to my ears the sound of tiny wings. The Oskereien were back from the Netherlands. Already?

Then followed a peculiar series of questions and answers. Since I could not tune my ears to the shrill voices of the Oskereien, the Finnish man with the great mustache assembled what they told him and related it to me.

"Mr. Santa What's-his-name there," said he with a finger poked in Santa's direction, "has a kind of a brother living in the Netherlands. Looks a bit like him but wears a white robe and a red cassock. On his head is a bishop's mitre, a tall, red one. He wears white gloves and carries a golden staff in his hand. He also wears an enormous bishop's ring on his left hand.

"He has a helper — *Zwarte Piet,* or Black Peter — whose color is black, for he is a Moor. Peter is dressed in a plumed hat, silken hose and doublet and he looks exactly like a medieval page from a far away land.

"Where do you suppose these two Christmas persons live? In the North Pole? No. They live in Spain! They come only once a year to the Netherlands, arriving on Sint Nicolaas Avond (that means St. Nicholas Eve) on December 5.

"The bearded Sint Nicolaas gives gifts out of a bag which Black Peter carries, and that includes switches which are given to children who are naughty. They arrive by boat, a steamer, which also brings a white horse which the Saint rides when he arrives. The ship docks at the harbor at Amsterdam while hundreds of children gather around and sing a song."

Here Wainamoinen directed a half dozen of the Oskereien to sing it for me. He admonished them to articulate clearly and to sing it slowly. Hence I understood the words, which were:

150

Look, there is the steamer from faraway lands.
It brings us Sint Nicolaas; he's waving his hands.
His horse is prancing on decks up and down;
His banners are waving in village and town.

Zwarte Piet is laughing. He tells everyone,
"The good ones get candy; the bad ones get none!"
Oh, please, dear Sint Nicolaas, if Pete and you would
Just visit our houses, we'll surely be good!

Wainamoinen looked pleased. "That is a fairly good report in a surprisingly short period of time, is it not? Saves you all the trouble of taking a trip, right? Now, is there anything else you want to know?"

I was intrigued by the Spanish character of Santa's counterpart in the Netherlands and, though I didn't wish to encourage the Finnish interloper, I asked why Sint Nicolaas was Spanish instead of Dutch.

Wainamoinen spoke shortly to the Oskereien, got an answer and relayed it to me.

"The Netherlands is a Protestant country, in the main," he said. "When it came time to learn about the gift giver of the Christmas period, Holland was a territory owned by the Holy Roman Empire. Later, it was occupied by the Spaniards under the rule of Philip II who was Spanish by birth and education. Philip's rule commenced in the year 1555. The Spanish ruled the Netherlands for many turbulent years. At last, in the year 1648, the Dutch Republic was recognized and Spain lost control. But they had occupied and ruled the Netherlands for 93 years — long enough to have an influence. And one of the influences was the Spanish character of Sint Nicolaas. He has never become a true Hollander."

I thought this was a rather good report. I turned to Santa Claus and whispered that I thought Wainamoinen did not intend that anything unpleasant should happen. Santa snorted.

151

I thought his blue eyes were filled with tears, but I did not look closely; I could not because it saddened me so. Then I whispered to him that he should chase these people — all of them — away.

"Chase them away!" he said, astounded. "They are here because of you! The damage is done now. You might just as well invite Der Belsnickel and Buzebergt and Budelfrau and Berchtel and Klaubauf and Befana. Yes, and the Joulupukki whom you like so well, and Père Fouettard who hit you with his stick. And why don't you invite Kris Kringle, too?" Santa spoke with great bitterness. "Invite all of them!"

Then instantly the air was filled with such a terrible noise and clatter that I had to cover my ears. I closed my eyes, too, because I was troubled about what I would see if they were open. Santa had accidentally invited a horde of gruesome Christmas monsters and demons. What now?

17

RETREAT TO SPAIN
AND POLAND

HE SIMPLE act of opening my eyes was also the act of plunging myself into a dreadful nightmare, for what I saw could not have been real. Everywhere about me were gnomes and monsters, hideous hags, animal-men, goblins, beasts and wretched figures out of pagan history.

They were everywhere — sitting on the Transvolo Stone, on the housetops, grouped in my yard and in my neighbors' yard. There were Oskereien in the trees, several forms of Grampus leaning against the house, wolf creatures bounding uncouthly in a ferocious game among themselves, at least three Klaubaufs from various places, one of them hanging from the boughs of my oak tree, his red tongue lolling out of his ugly, toothed mouth.

I saw Svaty Nikalas standing in the background as though undisturbed by this terrible scene. Cert was very much in evidence with his whip and his chain which he was rattling and shaking ominously at La Befana. There was the Joulupukki in hot pursuit of a haggish woman who I assumed was Berchtel or Budelfrau. Standing with hands on hips was Der Belsnickel, his body covered by sheets, his face hidden by a horrid mask.

Zwarte Piet was there, too, snapping his birch whip at one of the Nisser, and his kinsman, Black Peter, was helping him.

153

Then from the yard of my neighbors, I observed the familiar hairy figure of a Kallikantzeros from Greece. He was in the act of climbing the fence. When he entered my yard, he fixed me with one of the baleful looks I had come to know from the time of my visit to Greece. He started moving toward me. His attitude was threatening.

He was coming swiftly toward me. I am not ashamed to confess that I was frightened. It was the dreadful noises as much as the congress of so many hideous creatures. As I waited, I saw Grandfather Frost from the Soviet Union charge up from behind and give my adversary a great push forward. He crashed heavily into a Jultomten and they both fell into my frost covered flower beds. And there they thrashed wildly about, the large amber-eyed Greek monster pummeling the little Jultomten unmercifully.

As I watched in awe and fear, I observed Knecht Rupprecht rush to the aid of the Scandinavian goatman. Then, in quick succession, he was joined by an Aschenklas, a Pelzmarte, a Klapperbach, a Shem Koll from western Europe, a Habersack from the Hartz mountains, and a Mari Llwd from Wales. There they fought, fiercely snarling.

In the neighbor's yard I now observed a horse-like figure, perhaps a Schimmel, leap the fence and gallop toward the melee. Père Fouettard hurried toward the running, sheet-covered creature with the ugly horse's skull.

I heard a familiar voice in my ear, whispering. Frightened, I turned quickly to see that it was Grandma Babushka from the Soviet.

"It is better if you leave. Fast!" she whispered urgently.

It was then that I took Santa Claus, pale and trembling, by the hand. I made the incantation and said the name of a number of countries — I do not know which ones. I heard the sound of the familiar "whoosh" and felt motion. The ca-

154

cophony of discordant noises and shrieks in my backyard faded, and I found myself with Santa Claus—in Spain.

A pleasant voice — almost like music after the din and disorder in my own backyard at home — came to my ears.

"Feliz Navidad."

"Merry Christmas," I replied. I gave Santa a nudge to encourage him to offer a greeting, too. But he was upset. He said nothing.

"Where are we?" I asked the dark-haired, dark-eyed Spaniard who had spoken.

"You are here in the Monastery of Montserrat in Catalonia. It is, as you surely must know, Nochebuena, the Good Night, as Christmas Eve is called here. You are an American, I can see; but I do not know the country of your so gaily dressed friend."

"He is Dutch and American and I think Asian, too, or Turkish, and perhaps part Spanish," I replied with an attempt at humor.

Politely, our dark-haired man said nothing to this statement which must have been astounding to him.

"I am Juan Martínez Salzillo and at your service. We are about to have our Misa del Gallo. It is, as you would say, our Rooster Crow Mass because it is midnight, and then we shall have our great procession in honor of the image of the Black Virgin."

When I showed interest, Señor Martínez explained the story of the Black Virgin.

"It is a statue image of St. Mary, perhaps one of the oldest in the world. It is said that the figure was carved by St. Luke and brought to Barcelona, here in *España*, in the year A.D. 30 by none other than St. Peter during his European expedition."

The story of the Black Virgin, as told by Señor Martínez,

155

was somewhat legendary but believable. When the Moors invaded Spain sometime in the 700's, the image was hidden in a cave. And there it stayed, forgotten until 880. A church was erected there and the sacred relic was installed and enshrined on a marble throne.

Why is she called the Little Black Virgin? Because, said Señor Martínez, so many candles were burned near the image that smoke from them — hundreds and thousands of smoking candles—has turned the statue black. It is why the Spaniards call her La Morena, "The Dark Lady."

During Christmas festivals, the image is lifted onto a platform, surrounded by flowers and candles, and carried in a beautiful procession while a boys' choir chants ancient church songs.

Señor Martínez invited us to join the procession, but Santa Claus declared that there was not sufficient time. We had to be content with the brief explanation of the Spanish Christmas — *Pascua de Navidad,* Feast of the Birth — which comes on December 25.

It is a thoroughly religious festival in Spain. During part of the day at home, the service people visit patron after patron to leave cards or small verses and a greeting. To such doors come the garbage collectors, the carpenters, the delivery boys, the bakers, the shoemakers and others associated with service to the community. It is, of course, an indication of their wish to serve again during the coming year. Indeed, some of the servicemen who come to the door have not served their hosts at all, but wish to in the coming year. They are given modest presents in the spirit of the day, usually money.

Every home has its nacimiento, its crèche, or crib. Candles light them and children dance about them singing happy Christmas songs.

Spanish children expect their gifts at Epiphany, January 6,

which commemorates Christ's glory, a feast of the Baptism, the appearance of the Holy Dove and the voice from Heaven ("You are my beloved son, in whom I am well pleased"). The day is usually called "El Día de los Reyes" (day of the kings), a reference to the three wise men, kings or Magi, who brought gifts from the East to the Child Jesus.

Santa was so preoccupied that he did not seem interested in the long discussion of the giving of gifts. In Spain, said Señor Martínez, the children leave their shoes on the window sills or balconies and they are filled with straw and carrots or barley (cebada) for the horses of the Magi. Their favorite member of the Wise Men is Balthazar who rides a donkey. Their own presents, they believe, come mainly from Balthazar, and always include a bit of sweet candy called a turrón. It is believed the custom of giving such a sweet dates back to the ancient Roman custom of giving a sweetmeat to suggest that the coming year will be filled with good things.

Some Spanish people view the Magi as being camel riders and bringing gifts just as they did long ago at the time of the Nativity.

Señor Martínez sang a little Christmas song, a very old one, while Santa tugged impatiently at my sleeve; he wanted to return home to see what was transpiring in his territory and my backyard. The Song:

> Ay, Jesús mío,
> tu amor me inflame.
> Ay, ay, Jesús mío,
> tu amor me inflame;
> Pues ha salido para inflamarme!
> Ven, amor mío;
> ven, amor mío;
> ven, y no tardes;
> ven como sueles a consolarme!

Santa was so restless that it was necessary to excuse ourselves from the cordial Señor Martínez and walk to the corner of the church. There Santa suggested that we return. I was not sure it could be done without first visiting other places whose names I had mentioned in my troubled incantation. At any rate, I tried.

Despite careful wording, however, we were not routed directly home. We found ourselves in a little farming community near Sztum, Poland, and in front of a pleasant farmhouse. A young man, Roman Styczynski, called out a cheerful "Boze Narodzenie" and I returned the Merry Christmas greeting. Santa remained silent, troubled and anxious to return home.

Roman invited us into his home and explained some of the Christmas customs of Poland. He knew we would be interested in the rites of the *oplatki,* a kind of wafer which is made of flour and water, and with sacred figures stamped upon them. These are blessed by the local priest and eaten.

The Star of Bethlehem is a principal symbol in Christmastime Poland. The first star to appear in the evening sky on Christmas Eve is the signal that the long fast of Advent is over. At the time of the evening meal, the *oplatki* are eaten by every member of the family. This symbolizes the end of any family differences which might have taken place in the previous year, and it implies a fresh start with peace and understanding prevailing.

Oplatki are sent to the homes of friends and relatives, much as other people send Christmas cards.

Roman told us that his family had gone to visit relatives while he tended the farm animals and made other preparations for the coming Christmas festival. He had gathered straw and spread it upon the kitchen table to suggest the manger scene. He had spread a few bits of straw on the floor and stacked a sheaf against the wall in a corner of the room. He and his wife, he said, spread the straw because it is proper to do, and it brings "gross gluck" — great luck. Later, the straw and wheat are scattered among the farmers' fruit trees to help make the forthcoming fruit crop abundant.

Roman had also spent some hours visiting neighbors to see their *Joselki* (mangers) which have an important place in Polish festivities during the Christmas period.

The children, he told us, had already written letters to the Wise Men asking for their Christmastime gifts which come from the Magi on December 6 but are delivered to the home by "Star Boys," three young men of the village who carry a brightly lit star and sing carols as they distribute the gifts.

However, before the Polish children receive their presents, they are interviewed by a "Star Man" who determines if they know their catechism. In some sections of the country, the visit from the Star Man is followed by one from Svatej Nikulas, who may give the gifts; or by the Wise Men, or Three Kings (Tri Kralu). But the children must know their catechism or run the risk of getting a lump of coal instead of presents.

On Christmas Eve at midnight, all of Poland goes to its churches to hear the *Pasterka,* the Mass of Shepherds, Roman said. He invited us to join him and his family. Before I could get Santa Claus to agree to join them, there came a sharp knock on the door. Roman opened it upon two visitors — one, surely, was Svatej Nikulas and the other was apparently the "Star Man." Both glowered at us, particularly at Santa Claus.

Roman attempted to introduce us, but he foundered under the glare of the two latter visitors. At last Svatej Nikulas addressed us.

"I have heard in recent times that the American Santa Claus is interested in forming a coalition for concerted action against the Svatej Nikulas territory in Poland. Is this true?"

Dumbfounded, Santa merely shook his head in a bewildered negative.

"Nevertheless," Svatej said, "you have called a great meeting in the United States of all the Christmas figures of the world, have you not?"

"No, no!" I answered for Santa. "He did not call such a meeting. It was all a big mistake, a whole series of mistakes."

"Let him answer for himself," said the Star Man, shaking a large wooden six-pointed star in Santa's face.

"No," Santa said. "I am not forming a coalition for the purpose of invading Polish territory. And I have called no meeting."

"If so," said Svatej, "why are all of the world's Christmas

people and demons now meeting in your country? And why are you here? Did you hope that I would attend that meeting and that, in my absence, you would move into Poland as the principal gift giver?"

"No. Never has such a thought entered my mind," Santa said. "There were some Christmastime people assembled in the United States when we left, but we hurried away from such a meeting. Many of the people are not very nice, a strange condition for such a holy period, but some of them are creatures lingering over from the times of the heathens."

"Yes. I can see your plan quite clearly, however. You plan to get those people together as a united group and they could take over the Christmas of any country. Well, I will tell you this: They won't take over mine!"

I voiced an opinion here because I felt that Santa was not adequately defending himself against these unfair accusations.

"Santa doesn't want to take over Poland," I said. "He wants nothing more than to go home and protect his own territory. We didn't want such Christmas people in our country. And we don't want to take over Poland. Don't you understand that?"

"It seems to me that you people have a great deal of country to work in and perhaps you are looking for a smaller place — like Poland," said the Polish Santa. "It might be that I should have a good look at your territory and see if I should take over there."

Santa rolled his eyes and then looked at me. He signaled that we ought to go. But as we moved toward the door of Roman's cottage, the Star Man stepped into our path and blocked the way.

Roman apparently did not understand much of the foregoing, but he knew when violence appeared imminent.

"Now, Star Man, these people are our guests. Let them go if they want to."

The Star Man lifted his wooden star above his head as though to strike at us, but we hurried past him and out of the door. This time Santa made the wish, and successfully. Moments later we were at the Transvolo Stone in my backyard.

There was, indeed, a meeting going on. The yard was filled with people and creatures of every variety, but they were orderly and quiet. Someone had erected a lectern on the rock. And there, conducting the meeting, was a small man dressed somewhat in the manner of our Santa Claus.

"Who is he?" I whispered to Santa Claus as we were materializing.

"That's Samichlaus. He's from Switzerland."

Samichlaus was apparently calling the roll.

18

CHRISTMAS FIGURES, FAIR AND FOUL

S THE Swiss Samichlaus called the roll, a pretty lady sat beside him to keep the record of those present and those absent. She wore a small, round hat over her blond, braided hair. She wore a laced bodice and a silk apron.

"Who is she?" I whispered to Santa.

"That's Lucy. In Switzerland, the Samichlaus is married to Lucy, or Lucia, however you want to say it. So she is helping him keep the roll, just as a wife might help a husband."

Samichlaus shouted the names from a long list in front of him. Most of the Christmas people in attendance answered by saying "here" or "present" in their own language. Now and then, however, the response would be a scream or a howl or a bleat or a shriek.

I worried about what my neighbors might be thinking, but I could see none of them peering from windows so I thought that the strange people in my backyard might possibly be both invisible and unheard. I listened as Samichlaus shouted the names and I thought that this, indeed, would surely be the most curious assemblage in the history of Christmas. Samichlaus' voice was loud and clear.

"Weihnachtsmann from Germany!
"Svaty Nikalas from Czechoslovakia!

"Cert from Czechoslovakia!
"San Nicolà from Bari, Italy!
"Klapperbach from Usedom Island!
"Pelzmarte from Swabia!
"Aschenklas from Swabia!"

"Where," I asked Santa Claus, "is Swabia?"

"Oh, that's now part of Bavaria. It used to be a duchy in medieval days and included part of Switzerland. In German, it was called Schwaben. I imagine Samichlaus uses the old term for it because the creatures here date back to those days."

Santa and I had been noticed, of course, but nobody paid much attention to us. They seemed to be content with a glance at us.

Samichlaus continued:

"Schimmel from Silesia!
"Schimmelreiter from Pomerania!
"Papa Noël from Brazil!
"Shen Koll from Western Europe!
"Habersack from the Hartz Mountains!
"Josef from Silesia!
"Del Niño from Costa Rica!
"Father Christmas from England!
"Viejo Pascuero from Chile!
"Grampus from Austria!
"Klaubauf from Styria!"

I nudged Santa Claus. "Where is Styria? I don't think I've ever heard of it."

"That's a province of Austria. It's located in the Alps on the border of Yugoslavia."

And the crisp voice of Samichlaus continued to call:

"Bartell from Styria!
"Knecht Rupprecht from Germany!
"Black Peter from Holland!
"The Oskereien from Scandinavia!" (The air was shattered with

high pitched screaming.)
"Pelznickle from Germany!
"Ru-Klas from Germany!
"Wainamoinen from Finland!
"Budelfrau from Austria!
"Berchtel from Swabia!
"Befana from Italy!
"Joulupukki from Finland!
"Nikolo-Weibl from Bavaria!
"The Buttenmandl from Bavaria!" (Twelve voices cried "Here!")
"Nisse from Denmark!
"Grandpa Koleda from Bulgaria!
"Balthazar from Spain!
"The Camel from Syria!" (I heard a camel snort in response.)
"Jultomten from Sweden!
"Schmutzli from Austria!
"Jan Haas from Austria!
"Babushka from the Soviet Union!
"Grandfather Frost from the Soviet Union!
"Deydushka Moroz from the Soviet Union!
"Kallikantzeroi from Greece! (Hundreds of voices responded.)
"Fynnodderee from the Isle of Man!
"Domovy from the Soviet Union!
"Habergaiss from Styria!
"Old Hob from England!
"Hertha from Germany!
"Buzebergt from Augsburg!
"Ljeschi from the Soviet Union!
"Kris Kringle from Germany!
"St. Nikolas Thaumaturgis from Syria!
"Jul-Dokka from Sweden!
"Santa Claus from the United States! (Santa answered humbly.)
"Sinterklaas from Holland!
"Père Fouettard from Belgium!
"Père Fouettard from France!
"Zwarte Piet from the Netherlands!
"Père Noel from France!
"Balthazar, Gaspar, and Melchior from Spain!

"Star Man from Poland!" (He had come; he responded.)
"Svatej Nikulas from Poland!" (He, too, had come.)
"Los Reyes Magos from Spain!
"Pai Natale from Portugal!
"Tres Reyes Magos from Spain!" (Three voices answered.)
"Papai Noël from Brazil!
"Yeth from Devonshire!" (Dogs barked.)
"Frau Holda from Germany!
"Berchtel from the Tyrol!
"Fru Gode from Mecklenburg!
"Frau Frick from the Tyrol!
"Klas Bur from Holstein!
"Ru Klas from Mecklenburg!
"Christpuppe from Ruppin!
"The Feien from Ruppin!" (About 100 voices shouted "Here!")
"Segurocha from the Soviet Union!
"Bullerklas from Holstein!
"Gabriel from Silesia!
"Tomte Gube from Scandinavia!
"Kolyada from Russia!
"Lussi from Alsace!
"Klawes from Hanover!
"Klas Bur from Brunswick!"

The voice of Samichlaus went on and on. Through the various forms of the names like Nicholas he chanted, and through different versions of the names for saint and for bishop. It tended to be very confusing for me, but I was truly astounded to discover that there were so very many versions of Christmas figures, people and monsters and gnomes.

"Lan Khoong-Khoong from China!" Samichlaus shouted.
"Dun Che Lao Ren from China!
"Hoteiosho from Japan!"
Once again I nudged Santa Claus. "What strange versions of your name, Santa!"
"Oh," he said, "well, Lan Khoong-Khoong is Chinese for

Nice Old Man, and Dun Che Lao Ren translates to Christmas Old Man. The Japanese gift giver, Hoteiosho, was originally one of the old Japanese gods. They just borrowed him from their own background and had him double for their version of Santa Claus. They believe he has eyes in the back of his head so that he can see more easily when children are misbehaving."

I glanced over to the group of Orientals and observed that Hoteiosho truly did have eyes in the back of his head as well as in front.

The voice of Samichlaus had stopped. His wife, Lucy, was busily jotting things down on paper. At last she looked up at Samichlaus and said, "There are about two hundred people here, not counting monsters and goblins and Feiens and Heth and Oskereiens and gnomes."

Samichlaus relayed this information to the convention. "Now," he said, "we will keep this convention in order. We will function in a businesslike manner. There will be no violence, no biting or kicking of one another, no cutting people open, no screeching, screaming or shrieking. We will be orderly."

"Mr. Chairman." The voice was high and shrill.

"The chair recognizes the Nisse from Norway."

Norway's Julenisse, the pleasant little gnome who had been friendly with me, moved forward to a position where he could be seen.

"Mr. Chairman," he said in a reedlike voice, "this convention has established a set of by-laws which are not democratic and which I now protest."

"What element of the by-laws does the gentleman from Norway object to?" Samichlaus asked.

"I object to the undemocratic and unfair and inconsiderate portion of Section 2, Article 1, wherein it states that voting privileges shall be denied to all animals, all part-man-part-animals, all Heth, all Feien, all Oskereien, all gnomes, trolls, elfs, goblins, pigmies, manikins, and creatures of eerie or unwholesome manner and mien."

"I see," said Samichlaus. "Your point is well taken. I believe that the by-laws as presently written would deny you and other good gnomelike creatures the right of the vote. Is this your objection?"

"It most certainly is. I feel that a gnome is quite as good as the Buttenmandl from Bavaria, and better than Pelzmarte from Swabia."

Samichlaus nodded. Then he addressed himself to the gathering. "The gentleman from Norway believes that he and other gnomelike people should have the right to vote. He feels that he is a person, however small, and that he be given his franchise. Does the convention share his opinion? All in favor of granting this body the permission to alter or amend the by-laws, please signify by making the appropriate noises."

The noises, which includes "ayes," were mostly affirmative noises, although there were some negative sounds, too.

Samichlaus smiled down at the Julenisse.

"It appears that you shall have your way, and that you and other good-intentioned goblins shall have a vote."

The Nisse jumped forward.

"A point of order!" he shouted. "I ask that the by-laws be amended to grant the right to vote to the Nisse of Norway. I did not speak for any other gnome, such as the Jultomten or the Jul-Dokka of Sweden. And I certainly exclude from the right to vote the animal figure of the Julbuk, or Joulupukki, of Finland!"

There was immediate turmoil among the conventioners. The Julbuk leaped to his hind feet and was shouting, and the Jul-tomten was screaming loudly in protest.

Santa Claus motioned me toward the house. In the excite-

169

ment of the growing quarrel, we sidled unnoticed around to the front of my house and inside. Once there, Santa Claus looked steadily into my eyes.

"I think you know how all of this trouble has come about, do you not?"

I nodded, although I held the belief that I had not literally caused the trouble. It had happened due to no deliberate wrong on my part. However, I saw no reason to quibble. I had enough of that.

"Very well," Santa said. "Do you side with me? Do you wish me to remain as Santa Claus or would you prefer to have me substituted by someone else — a goat perhaps, or a horse's skull?"

"I am with you, Santa. I am certainly with you."

"Good," he said. "Now let us make a plan."

So, while the commotion outside continued, Santa Claus prepared a speech which, I am pleased to say, he asked me to help him with. But he had other ideas, too, which he did not wish to discuss, he said. Not yet.

19

LAST WISH

OMETIME during the long night of contention outside of the house and of invention inside the house, the problem of whether all gnomes had an equal vote was settled. They had won the right. Santa Claus had worked on the speech he planned to give during the convention, and he had also worked on a set of charts which he did not let me see. At last it was dawn.

Outside, the convention business was commencing. I heard the voice of the Weihnachtsmann from Germany:

". . . so it is not a question of aggression against the provinces controlled by the gift giver of the United States. We all abhor acquisition by power rather than by negotiation and adjudication. But the question is whether the American Weihnachtsmann does properly and generously provide for the children in this territory. We of Germany do not think in terms of invasion, but of assistance. We hold the good of the children of the world to be of prime importance.

"We point with pride to the fact that many portions of the American Christmas have been borrowed — I shall not say stolen — from Germany. So I may say to you that when the time comes to vote for a replacement for Santa Claus, it is I, the German Weihnachtsmann, who could most ably replace him. I ask for your support."

There was some applause as there is after every political speech, but it was desultory. Some of the German monsters made dreadful noises which were, I think, of approval. But it was not easy to tell.

Samichlaus rapped his gavel for order. When the motley crowd became silent, Balthazar from Spain asked to speak. He was dark-haired and well-mannered. His voice was deep and cultured.

"In my part of Spain, as elsewhere in the world, I — Balthazar — am the giver of gifts. I am assisted by two others, Gaspar and Melchior. Together we are known as the Three Wise Men. Need I point out that in times such as these, we are in need of wisdom? Where else, may I ask you, can one find three persons so ably suited to be the gift givers idolized by the children of the world?

"Where else among all the nations of the world are there men more closely associated with the Nativity and all of its goodness? Who else, I ask, *found* the Christ Child? We did — Balthazar, Gaspar and Melchior! *We* went out and searched; *we* followed the star. *We* disdained hardships and suffering to find the Child in the manger, and by so doing *we* have brought more good into the world than it ever had before.

"Therefore, when you vote for a substitute for Santa Claus, you will do well if you vote for not one, but for three men — each of them wise."

At this point, Santa Claus rose to be recognized.

There was a question about whether or not he should be permitted to speak. Some of the conventioners opposed it bitterly and loudly. Others declared that it was only fair that he be given an opportunity to defend his territory.

Samichlaus was a good chairman. He guided the objectors to at least a reluctant agreement. Then he moved aside and permitted Santa Claus to speak. I was very surprised at Santa's congenial manner and also at what he said.

"Gentlemen. Ladies." He smiled broadly, and his face was a picture of happiness and jollity.

"I do not choose this moment to ask for your consideration or your vote. Instead, I wish to welcome you to my territory — or at least what once was my territory."

There was some laughter in the crowd. Some of it was malevolent and some of it was merely good humor. Santa laughed, too. His face was red and full of good humor. His long beard was freshly combed and groomed, and his clothes were impeccable. He commanded much favorable attention. He continued.

"I would be a poor host indeed if I did not welcome you all — everybody — to the United States. Had I been here at the time of your arrival, I would have been much better prepared to show you that you are welcome here. I know your purpose is to better the world, to make it a finer, happier place to live in. And that is my purpose, too. If it can be shown that any person is better able to serve children than I have done, I will gladly and without opposition give up my place here and go elsewhere. Perhaps I should go to the Netherlands which is where I once lived. Perhaps I should go to Bari where Saint Nick served in a church as a bishop and where — excuse my immodesty — where Saint Nick became a saint.

"Perhaps I should go to Germany whence many of my customs and even some of my habits have come — where the world got the splendid thought of having Christmas trees. Perhaps I should go to Czechoslovakia which I love, or to Poland where some of my achievements here have been copied. Perhaps, if I am replaced here in the United States, I might go to Japan or to China where all of my customs have been duplicated.

"Well," he said smiling shyly, "I suppose the children of

almost any place might find me at least a little attractive." He
paused for a full thirty seconds, and he added, "I have not been
unloved."

Quickly, I assessed Santa's speech so far. He had been jolly
and hospitable and had thus won some friends in the convention. And he had also used a veiled threat. He might go
elsewhere!

Santa was delivering a master's stroke here. With each men-
tion of a different place he might go to, there was some dissatis-

fied mumbling. Surely, thought the Weihnachstmann of Germany, it would not do to have such a personable man in Germany. It was obviously the intention of the Weihnachtsmann — as well as all of the others — to take over Santa's territory, yet to keep their own for themselves.

Santa went on and on, always cheerful, always modest, but always adding another and still another country to the list of places to which he might like to go if he were overthrown here. People love their own lands; they always do. And to none of them was it attractive that Santa's willingness to abdicate suggested a take-over of their own country.

Santa spoke on and on about how happy he was that all of these people from "so many beautiful lands which I love" had come to visit his territory, and to pay him the compliment of loving it above their own lands!

Again he paused for a long half-minute. When he spoke, he spoke with great gentleness and kindness.

"Friends," he said, "because I was not here when your convention commenced, I was unable to show you the hospitality and kindness which is part of my upbringing. Now, because I have been in contact with my Brownies at the North Pole, I am able to present to each and everyone of you some modest gifts. They will, I hope, help to assure you that you are welcome."

The conventioners said pleasant things, like "ahhhhh," for the thought of a gift or two was attractive to them as it is to almost everybody. Gift giving was important to this convention.

"Therefore," said Santa, "I move that this convention be adjourned for a few hours while we — my Brownies and I — give you the gifts of hospitality." He sat down.

The applause was instant and surprising. Santa had been extremely effective.

Santa whispered some directions to Chairman Samichlaus

who announced that the gifts would be presented by groups, and that each group should move to the portion of my backyard where their names and classifications were inscribed upon signs which the Brownies would bring in.

The meeting was brought to a close. It would reconvene in two hours, Samichlaus said.

Now the Brownies came. There were dozens of them, more than I had ever thought existed. Some were bearing signs, and some were bearing gifts wrapped in lovely Christmas paper. Others came pushing steam tables and foods of every variety, each labeled according to the ethnic group it might best please. The Brownies were neatly. groomed and extremely polite to everyone.

Santa Claus invited me to stroll around to the various groups which had been assembled by his direction. He smiled and shook hands with everybody, even some of the monstrous creatures like the Schmutzli and the Schimmel and the Habergaiss and the Kallikantzeroi who tried to bite him. He even took the paw of one of the Heth! It was very brave of Santa. He was being a gracious host.

But I noted something. Each of the Christmas people had now gone into a group of his own kind. All of the various forms of bishops were seated congenially together. All of the most monstrous ones were in their own group. The several kinds of people who looked somewhat like Santa Claus were, somehow, sitting side by side. Among them were England's Father Christmas and the ones from other British Isles; there were people like the Swiss Samichlaus, and Svaty Nikalas from Czechoslovakia, Kris Kringle from Germany, Svaty Nikalas from Poland and Deyushka Moroz of Russia.

Most of the women were gathered together, too, but they proved to be unlike and there were quarrels going on continuously. But, as Santa pointed out to me, it is not easy to

176

place pretty St. Lucy (nine of them) with wrinkled old hags like Befana and Berchtel and Budelfrau and Frau Frick and Fru Gode and expect perfect harmony. "They are too different," Santa said. And they were.

But in other areas, Santa had planned quite well, I thought. For example, he did not put the camels with the animals; he put them with the various Wise Men from the several countries which employ them. He did so because camels are frightened of monsters and because the Wise Men know and understand camels even if they do not like them. These camels, however, were somewhat superior. In certain countries, like Syria, the camel is the gift giver as Santa Claus is in the United States.

In Syria, they regard their Christmas camel as the gentle camel of Jesus. Their legend has it that this was the youngest camel among those which brought the Wise Men to the Child. It achieved immortality and was placed in the role of gift giver. For naughty children, according to the Syrian legend, the camel has no presents. Instead he places a black mark on their wrists.

Santa had thought of food specialties for everybody. There were Lussikakes for the members of the Lucy section, boars' heads for the English, ham hocks and sauerkraut for the Germans, haggis for the Scots, kolage for the Czechs, julekake for the Danes, buñuelos for the South Americans, boulgeur pilav for the Armenians and something for everybody.

And for each group, Santa had chosen an American food to give them all an idea of what Americans eat. For this he chose sloppy joes, a mixture of ground hamburger meat, mixed onions, catsup, seasoning of various kinds and chopped green peppers. I thought he might have chosen another, better food, as being representative of our country. But Santa's planning so far had been exemplary; I would not protest.

Every person or creature in attendance received a gift from Santa, a whistle hand carved and fashioned from a willow branch. I thought this, too, was peculiar, but I do not believe that I am wiser than a man who has lived for so many years and who has known so many different people. I kept my silence.

At last the meeting was called to order. People spoke on their own behalf, of course, and asked for the support of the convention when it came time to vote. Each speaker had kind things to say about Santa's hospitality, and about the good food. Each noted, in passing, that the food from their own country seemed infinitely more palatable and tasty than the sloppy joes of the United States. But it was said, always, in good humor.

Last to speak was Santa Claus. He approached the stand with a more serious look upon his face than he had had before. The convention, now in a much better mood than at the outset, rose to applaud him as he commenced his address.

"You will wonder, perhaps, why you were assembled into groups of your own kind. I chose this method of showing you that we Christmas people are all related in our own way. Besides, sooner or later you would have of your own accord, gathered together among your own kind. You note that the numerous representatives of St. Lucy, St. Lussi, Santa Lucia, and so on, are now together though they were grouped with women.

"Please note also that the Budelfraus are together with the Frau Fricks and the Berchtels and the Frau Holdas; that the angels like Gabriel are together; that the Wise Men are with the Magi and the Tres Reyes Magos, and that they are apparently happy there.

"Though originally the Joulupukki was placed with the animals, he has seen fit to move over and join his human associates from the Scandinavian countries. His goat costume covers a man.

"The monsters are together and have remained together as

you see. They have, apparently, eaten so much food from their own plates and from the plates of others that they are now sound asleep. Surely they must have eaten most of the sloppy joes which were placed before you! Let them slumber there like sated beasts.

"Those of us who have a vote according to the by-laws of this convention are fundamentally good people. You love children above all else. Samichlaus and Svaty Nikalas and Father Christmas and Grandfather Frost and Papa Noël and Grandpa Kolenda and Sinterklaas and Svaty Nikalas and Père Noël are not very different. They are, instead, as one man. Look at them; look at us!"

He waited. I looked over the group he mentioned, and there was a remarkable resemblance among them. They were as brothers! Some were dressed a little differently but each had red cheeks, white whiskers, and fur trimmed red cloaks. Santa Claus and Grandfather Frost were almost identical to Papa Noël and Father Christmas. And all had a jolly manner. It was a strange and wonderful revelation! The world seemed to me to be smaller and less complex than ever before. And here was proof before my eyes — the WORLD is indeed related at Christmas!

The members of the Lucy family were the same! The gnomes and the elves and the trolls were almost indentical! Black Peter and Zwarte Piet were twins! So were the Pères Fouettard!

Even the monsters had remarkable similarities. The Schimmel were very much like the Kallikantzeroi, and Old Hob looked and acted like the Schimmel though they lived in countries far apart.

I could see no difference at all in the Wise Men.

The Oskereien were precisely like the Russian Domovy and the Ljeschi and the Eien!

Members at the convention were now standing and looking about them. They were awed by the likeness among themselves and the creatures of Christmas. Now, with the entire convention standing surprised and impressed, Santa continued.

"A very long time ago," he said, "before the Renaissance, the people were uncultured, unlearned, and unkind. The lives they led were filled with cruelties. They slaved and were serfs and peons, and they were rewarded for their labors with kicks and brutalities. It was natural that they themselves would think in cruel terms.

"But the world's people are wiser now, and gentler. The cruel thoughts have faded away behind our learning and education and efforts to understand one another. Cruelty is no longer proper nor acceptable in the world."

"We do not need to torture our children into good behavior. Our love is sufficient to guide them to righteousness. Our kindness serves as an example of what they must grow to do. No longer do we need werewolves and Schimmels and Fynnodderes, or beasts with sharp teeth and wolves' bodies! They are of the past; they do not now nor have they ever deserved to be a true part of Christmas! Shall we dismiss them now and forever?"

The applause was thunderous. It was clear that the convention was of one mind on this score.

But Santa went on. "Let the evil creatures who threaten and bully and chastise little children be released from their cruel duties at the Christmas festival!"

At this, Santa stood long and silently as if waiting. The moments passed and time became oppressive and heavy. The conventioners seemed to grow tense and restive. And once again I suspected that Santa was making a mistake. He had been eloquent and persuasive and he had won his audience. But now he stood there silent, unmoving. I tried to guess his motive. At last he spoke again, his voice low.

"Shall we dismiss the evil creatures or shall we suffer them to add horror and shame and degradation to the most beautiful time of the world?"

Again he waited. But this time the pause was meaningful. He stood there at the podium, his manner serious, his eyes searching the crowd. And his silence became eloquent. People stirred.

First the Joulupukki from Finland rose and stepped to the Transvolo Stone. He muttered some words and quickly stepped down. I heard the familiar whooshing sound and wondered what had happened. I glanced about me and discovered that the tiny, malevolent Oskereien were disintegrating and fading away!

Josef from Silesia rose next and stepped to the Transvolo Stone. He, too, spoke softly. The Schimmel faded away with the familiar whooshing sound. Then came Kris Kringle from Germany who spoke softly. Great sounds filled the air! And when I looked to see what had happened, I saw that he had caused the disappearance of the wretched Pelznickles, the Ru-Klases, the Nikolo-Wiebels, and the Buttenmandls.

And so it went. One by one the congenial kinds of Christmas people rose and had their say on the Transvolo Stone, and the crowd thinned until only gentle people remained.

A feeling of awe came over me. I knew I was taking part in a most profound historical change, one which was to alter the world and the ways of it. The gentle people of the convention who remained sat in strange silence as though contemplating what might occur in the days to come.

Perhaps, I thought, their minds raced over the ideas which had come to mine. And perhaps, too, they wondered about the evil people and creatures who had for so many hundreds of years instilled fear in the minds of little children. Would they, or could they, return? Might it be possible that they could some day obtain possession of the Transvolo Stone and use it to influence and spoil the world of good people and joyous Christmases? I knew that I was unable to guess. My thoughts took the form of hope. But, troubled as I was, I dismissed such things from my mind when I noted Santa Claus walking once more to the Transvolo Stone to finish his speech.

"Friends," he said in solemn tones, "if it is proper that you should take over the duties of the gift giver of the United States, I shall not say that you may not. But I do not think that it is your desire to do so. Nor is it my desire to move into your lands to serve your children."

Once again he paused.

"And I shall tell you why," he said as though he had made a crisp decision. "Once I believed that there should be one gift giver — a good, kind person who would serve all of the world. But today I have learned that Father Christmas of England and Svaty Nikalas of Poland and Czechoslavakia and Papai Noël of Brazil and Viejo Pascuero of Chile and Grandfather Frost of the Soviet Union and all of the others — they are as I am and I am as they are.

"We are one, you and I, each of us, with gentle people to aid us and to teach our children that the world is well and good, and for them to revere and love as they have been taught to love and to trust and to know no fear.

"Friends," he said, "we came to this place with jealousy and avarice in our minds. We depart with understanding and with love — and with hopes for the world at Christmas."

I expected great applause when Santa walked away from the Transvolo Stone, but there was none. But I somehow understood that the gathered people were deeply touched with what he had said and how he had said it. Applause was not needed nor expected; the deep, thoughtful silence which filled the air was great praise, indeed.

And soon, one by one, our guests departed. Santa Claus climbed into his sleigh and waved cheerily to me as he mounted to the sky. I knew he was happier then he had ever been before. So was I, and filled with awe at what had transpired.

I confess that I worried a little about my neighbors and what they thought about the strange convention in my backyard. Though I was tired and overwhelmed with the events of the great day, I wandered my way through the neighborhood to visit them. I discovered that I was in no difficulty. A few of them hinted that it was rather odd that I had not invited them to the masquerade party in my yard, but I gave them no falsehood in return. If my silence was equal to a falsehood, this book may explain the truth.

Tired and weary, I wandered toward my home in the gathering dusk. I walked slowly to the Transvolo Stone and pondered for a moment. Then I stepped upon it and spoke the incantation and made my wish. At last I went into the house and to bed and to sleep.

Slumber came swiftly and was deep and restful. Hours later in the gray dawn I awoke and rose. I walked to the window and looked out to see if the Transvolo Stone had done anything unusual during the night. It had.

It had disappeared.

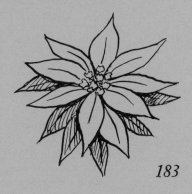

183